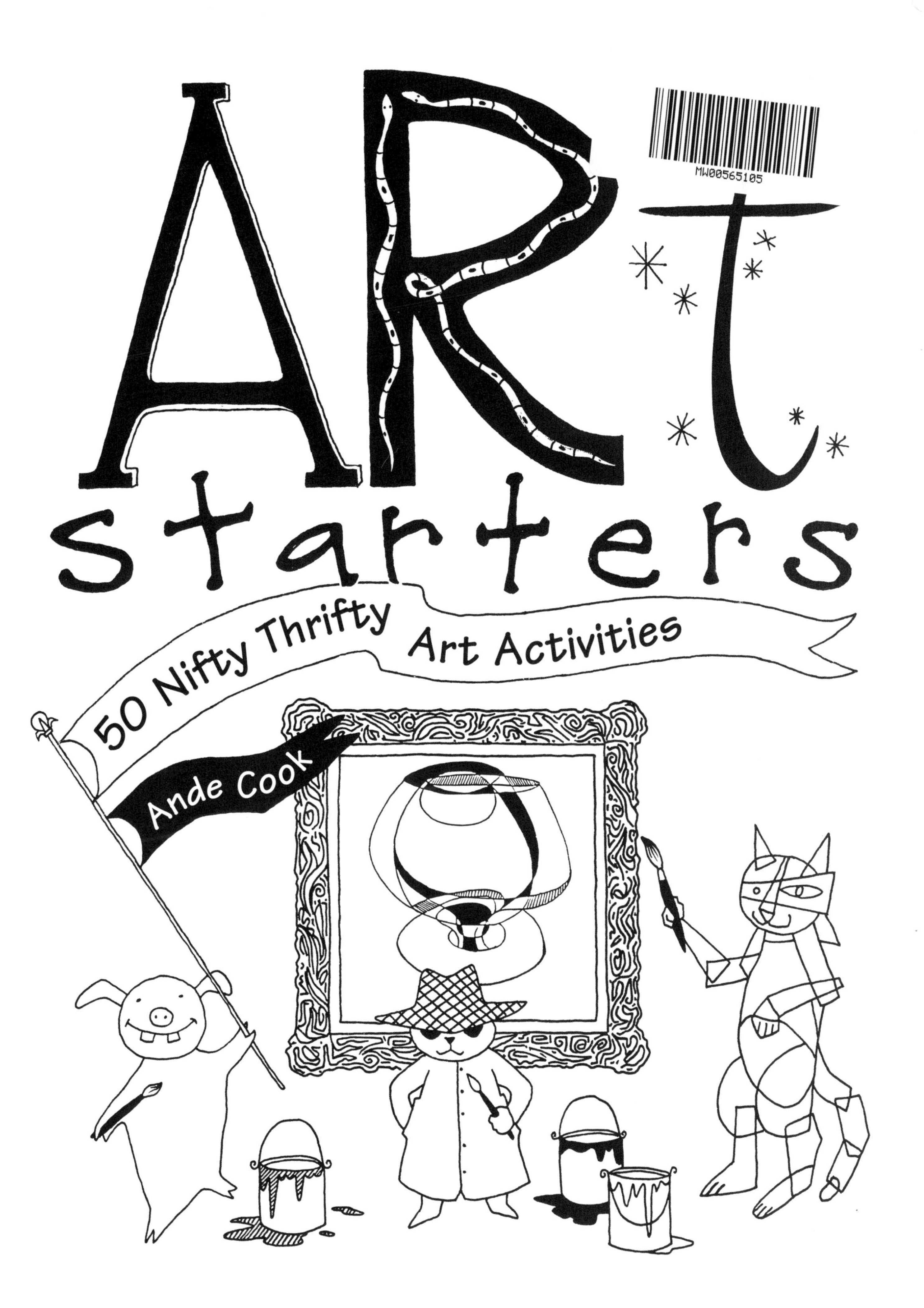
ARt
starters
50 Nifty Thrifty Art Activities
Ande Cook
MW00565105

Printed in the United States of America
ISBN 0-87192-303-3

10 9 8 7 6 5 4 3

Dear Teachers and Parents:

ArtStarters are part of an expanding collection of art activities I began for my students in 1987. **ArtStarters** mix philosophy, process, vocabulary and art history facts with entertaining illustrations. They are an effective vehicle for delivering art ideas and information to students of all ages and provide creative entertainment for children at home.

This book contains some of my best **ArtStarters.** They include games, quizzes and worksheets; facts from history; drawing, painting and mixed-media activities; "tip" and reference sheets; art from around the world; and a few of my all-time favorite art projects. Their versatility allows easy adaptation to suit a wide range of purposes and ability. The single-page format lends itself to quick photocopying for distribution in the classroom. **ArtStarters** can be used as rainy-day activites at home or as enrichment for formal art lessons, homework and extra-credit assignments. Substitute teachers find them useful as ready-made lesson plans or activities for students who finish in-class assignments early.

I hope you will find **ArtStarters** a helpful and enjoyable group of activities for your kids.

Best Wishes

Ande Cook

Contents

Several **ArtStarters** are versatile enough to appear under more than one category.

For example, page 36, **Aboriginal Design** is listed under both "Drawing" and "Painting," because either medium can be used depending on the mood of the day. We hope the multiple listing of **ArtStarters** adds flexibility to your fun!

Design

A Fun Game	7
The Design Elements	8
Quiz—Elements and Principles of Design	9
Language Art	14
Legal Graffiti	15
Pictography	16
The Dog's Domain	17
Poster Design	18
Menu Madness	19
Make a Board Game	20
The Art Museum Game	21

Drawing

A Fun Game	7
Adventures in Line	10
Adventures in Value	11
More Adventures in Value	12
A Balancing Act	13
Language Art	14
Flip Book I	22
Flip Book II	23
Drawing People	24
Gesture Drawing	25
Drawing Faces	26
Drawing Masks	27

Blind Contour Drawing	28
Wind Blend	29
The Style Game	30
Abstract Expressionism	31
A Cubist Drawing	32
Limitation	33
Animal Abstraction I	34
Animal Abstraction II	35
Aboriginal Design	36
The Circle Game	37
Clouds	45
Trees—Structure	46
Trees—Foliage	47
Islamic Architecture	48

Other Techniques

Press On	38
Frottage	39
Sanded Crayon Drawing	40

Color

Language Art	14
Frottage	39
Sanded Crayon Drawing	40

There's more →

What About Color ? 41
Colored Pencils 42
The Seven Snake Quiz 43
More Adventures in Line 50
Accordian Books 51

Painting

Abstract Expressionism 31
Aboriginal Design 36
Ink Washes 44
Clouds 45
Trees—Structure 46
Trees—Foliage 47

Architecture

Islamic Architecture 48
Architectural Detail Hunt 49
More Adventures in Line 50

3-Dimensional Projects

Adventures in Line 10
Accordian Books 51
Mask 52
Great Stuffed Fish 53
Day of the Dead 54
Papel Picado 55

A Fun Game

See if you can draw:

1. Someone really tall
2. Someone really small
3. Someone part machine
4. Someone part wild thing
5. Someone in a crazy hat
6. Someone with a kitty cat
7. Someone who just goes & goes
8. Someone with a great big nose
9. Someone who lives in the sea
10. Someone who looks just like me.

* **Don't make your drawing <u>anything</u> like the examples below.**

The Design Elements

- **Line** is the most versatile and necessary of all the graphic elements.

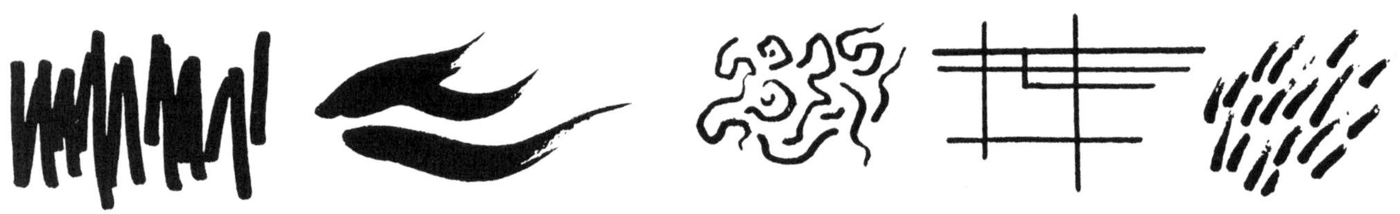

Look at lines in art by Paul Klee, Franz Kline, Jean-Michel Basquiat, Vincent van Gogh and Cy Twombly.

- **Shapes** are areas contained by lines; they can be outlined or solid. Shapes overlapped or shaded will look three-dimensional and become forms. Sculptures are forms.

Look at shapes in art by Henri Matisse, Jacob Lawrence, Stuart Davis and Robert Motherwell.

- **Value** refers to the lightness or darkness of an object or area. You get various values by shading.

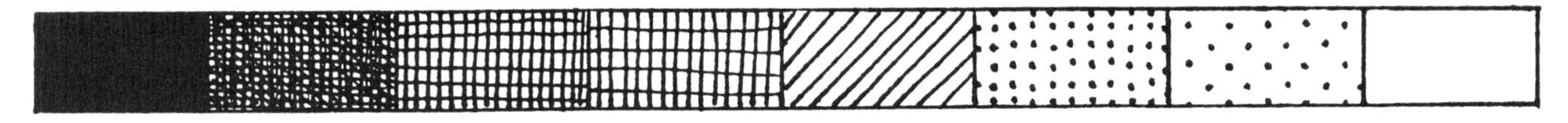

Look at value in art by Lyonel Feininger, Marcel Duchamp, Cubist portraits by Pablo Picasso, Georges Braque, Juan Gris and Georges Seurat.

- **Texture** is how something feels or looks like it feels. Simulated texture is an illusion the artist creates on a flat surface, often by creating patterns.

Look at texture in art by Vincent van Gogh, Lucas Samaras, Max Ernst and Romare Bearden.

- **Space** indicates a feeling of depth on a two-dimensional surface. Space also refers to areas designated as positive or negative.

Look at space in art by Ellsworth Kelly, Al Held, Renaissance painters (linear perspective).

- But what about **Color?** See page 41.

Quiz

Elements and Principles of Design

Match the terms at right with the appropriate illustration below.

__ 1 asymmetrical balance
__ 2 one-point perspective
__ 3 texture
__ 4 rhythm
__ 5 radial balance
__ 6 form
__ 7 repetition
__ 8 symmetry
__ 9 value
__ 10 depth
__ 11 variation
__ 12 two-point perspective
__ 13 movement
__ 14 shape
__ 15 line

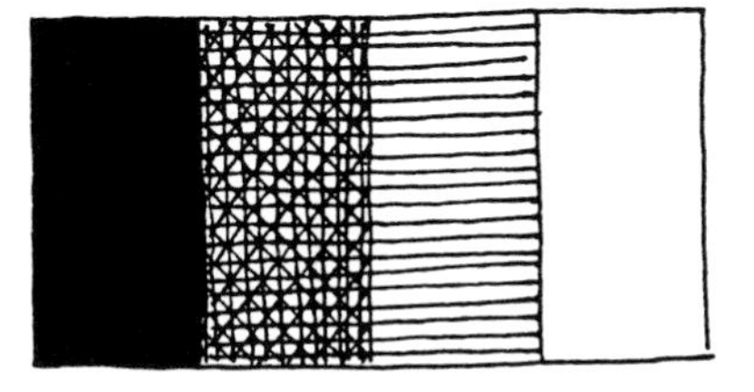
a.

b.

c.

d.

e.

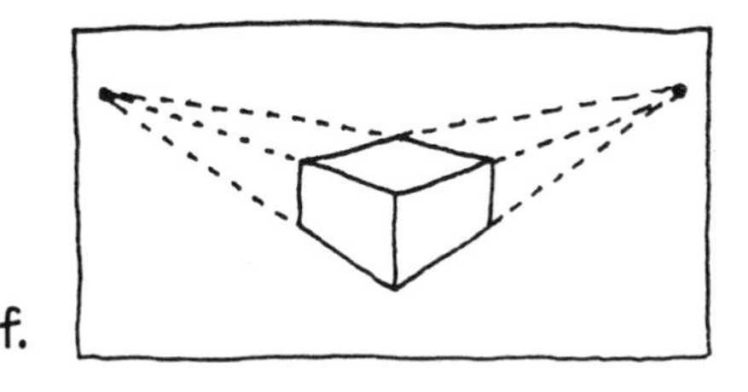
f.

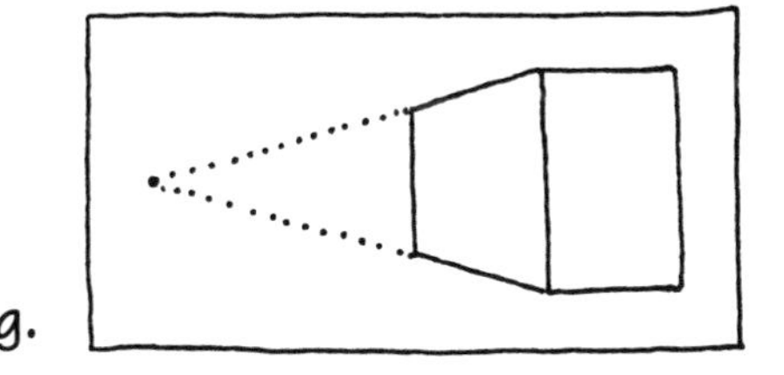
g.

h.

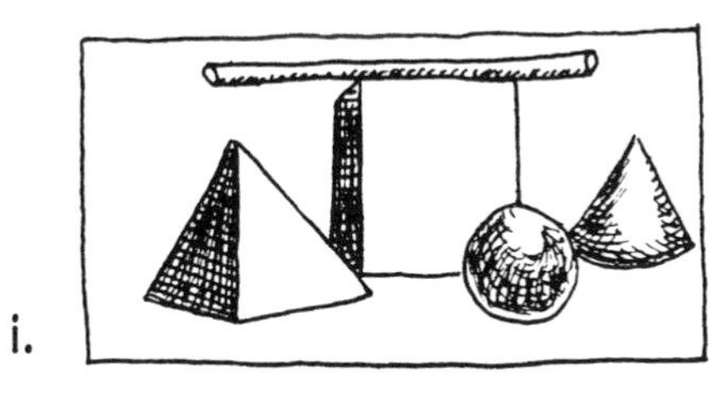
i.

j.

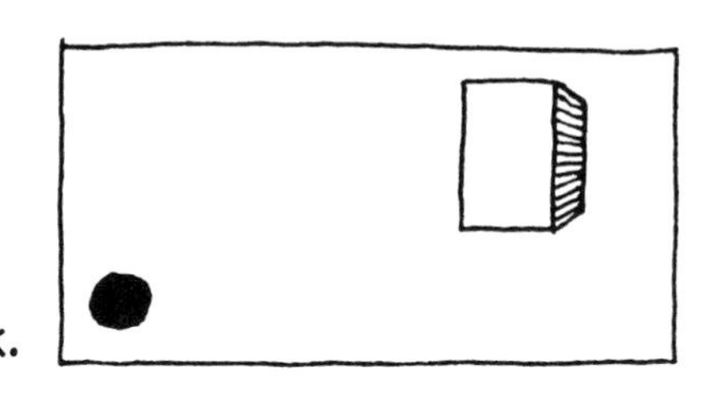
k.

l.

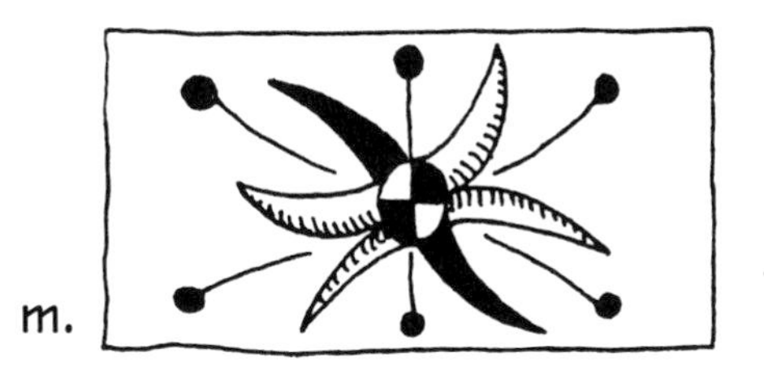
m.

n.

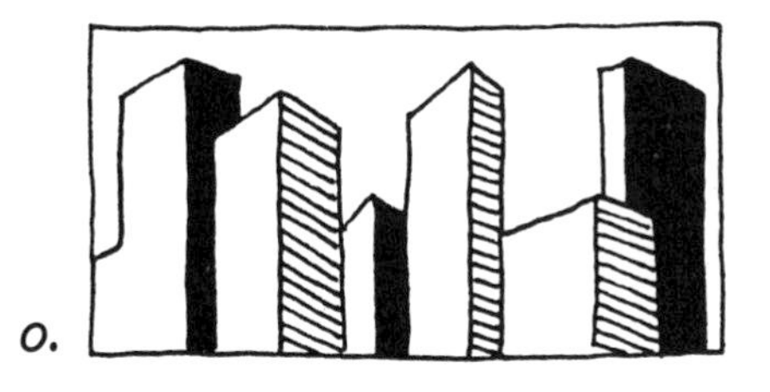
o.

Key: 1. k, 2. g, 3. j, 4. b, 5. m, 6. i, 7. o, 8. l, 9. a, 10. n, 11. e, 12. f, 13. h, 14. c, 15. d

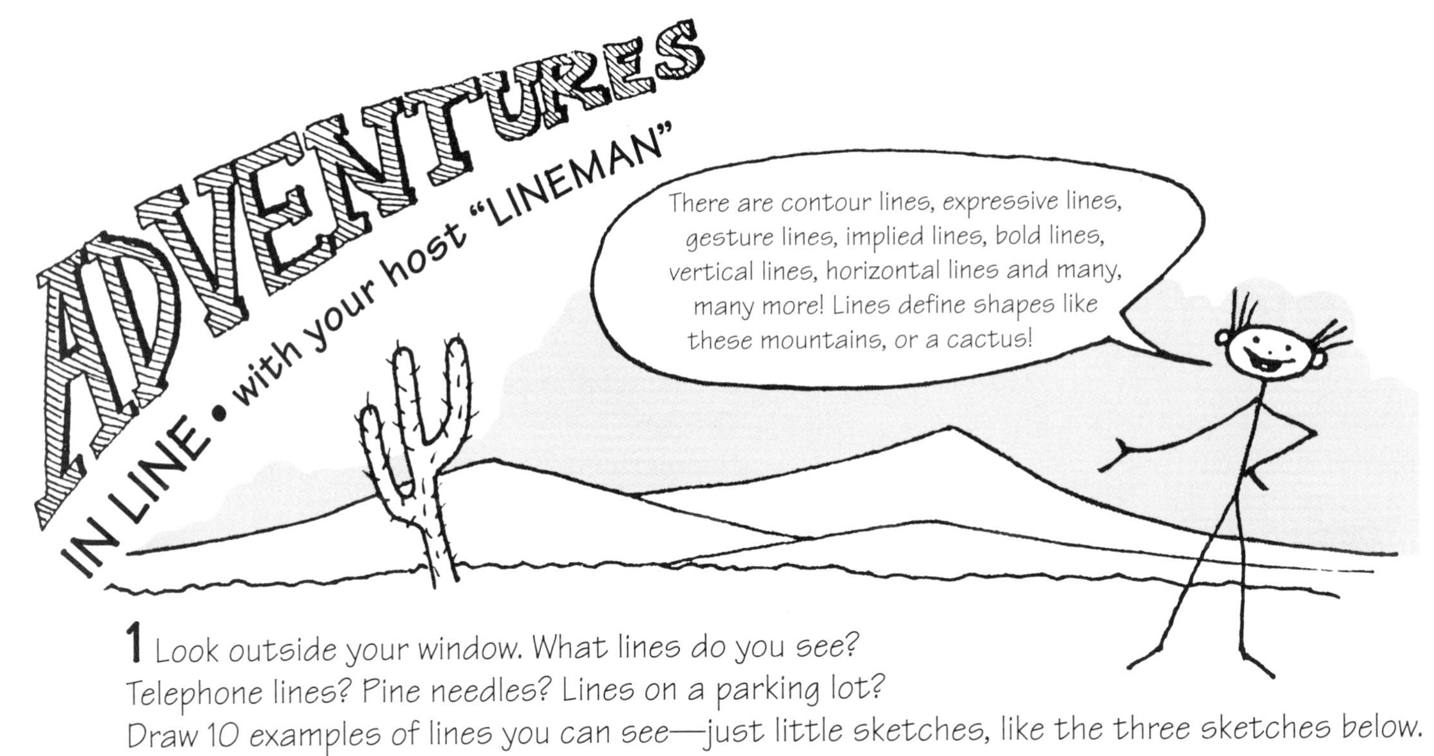

1 Look outside your window. What lines do you see? Telephone lines? Pine needles? Lines on a parking lot? Draw 10 examples of lines you can see—just little sketches, like the three sketches below.

a winter tree

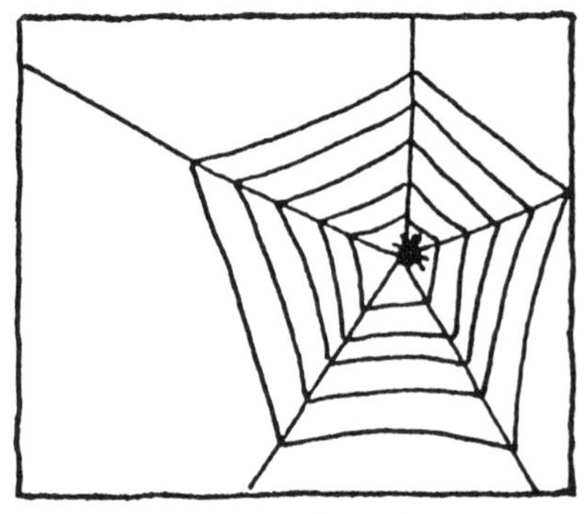

a spider's web

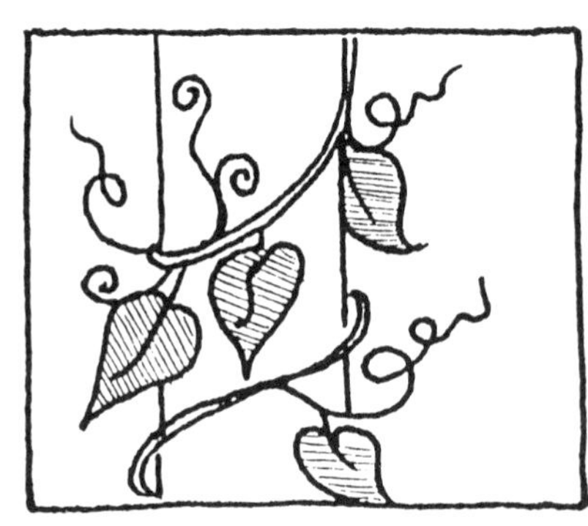

a climbing vine

2 Do some drawings using <u>one continuous line</u>. The monkey head on the right shows where the line starts **(S)** and ends **(E)**. In a continuous line drawing, you don't pick up your drawing tool from beginning to end! Try it using a crayon and large paper, like newsprint. Don't think about it too much, and stay loose. You should do it kind of <u>fast</u>—and practice. When you get the hang of it, you will love it!

*** Tip:** follow my line with your pencil, and you will get the feel of it.

3 I'm riding one of Alexander Calder's wire sculptures. A wire sculpture is like a contour line drawing in space. Try making a wire sculpture from one of your drawings. For inspiration, check out some books on Alexander Calder, like "Calder's Universe". Look at the "Circus" wire sculptures. Wow! You can make your sculptures with pipe cleaners or telephone wire or Twist-eez™. Try it!

SOW (1928)

ADVENTURES IN VALUE

with Shady Character

Shading drawings creates a range of light and dark values. Value is what gives a flat drawing dimension. The term **chiaroscuro** refers to the light and shadow, reflections and cast shadows visible in a drawing or painting.

Drawings with strong, dark values that **contrast** with lighter areas look better than drawings that are shaded in a middle gray.

When shading with a pencil, try working with textured papers or illustration boards like coquille. Experiment with softer pencils like a 4B or an ebony pencil. Always build up a value gradually for an even tone and richness.

Do a simple line drawing of objects. Shade the objects so they look three-dimensional. (You can set up an actual still life for this drawing. It's not too much trouble, and you will see how light and shadow work!)

Value doesn't have to be used to create dimension; it can be a design tool.

Shady's Value Hall of Fame

- Georges Seurat prepared for his famous painting "Sunday Afternoon on the Isle de Grande-Jatte" with a series of value drawings. Objects and edges are soft so you hardly see a line.

- Chris Van Allsburg illustrated the Caldecott award-winning "The Garden of Abdul Gasazi" with a No. 2 pencil and white drawing paper. All his drawings include solid blacks and whites with many, many values in between. Check this book out!

- M. C. Esher's lithographs and drawings are rich in values. He used patterns and lines in lino and woodcuts to create value and texture.

Shade Forms: put the light source (sun) where ever you want, and shade the forms below. Use cross-hatch, diagonal lines, waves, spirals, circles, whatever you want to create different values.

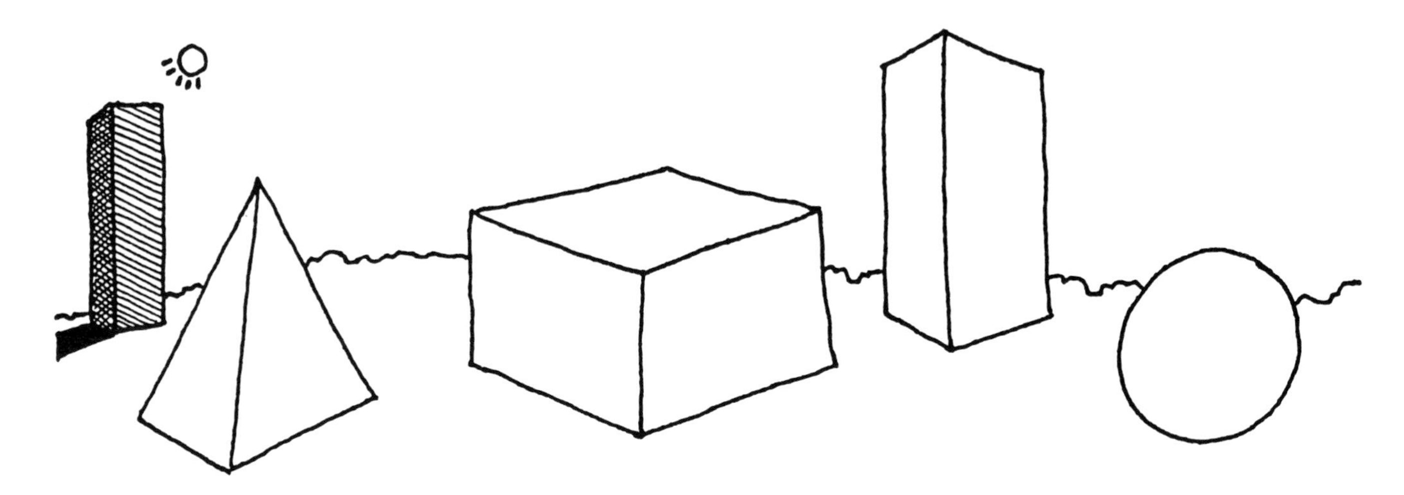

Value Scale: go from dark to light as smoothly as possible. Blend evenly. Try not to show any pencil lines. When you finish, you should have five very different values. * **Tip:** build up value gradually.

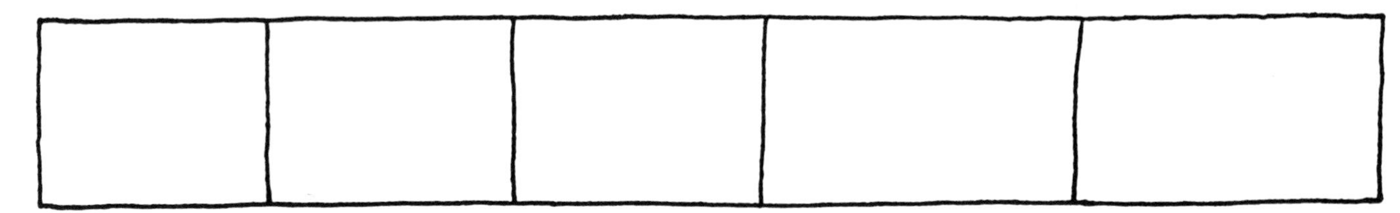

A BALANCING ACT

See if you can draw a stack of things and make it look **balanced.** Draw stacks of animals, people and things, or combine all three! Draw real-life stacks like junkyard cars, birthday presents and dirty dishes. Imaginary stacks present many possibilities. Draw five stacks, and try lots of different subjects. Or, try making one really tall stack. It's a challenge.

Balance depends on making sure weight is even on both sides. If part of your drawing moves to the far right, balance it on the left. Don't let the drawing lean. Draw straight up.

Language Art

This is an old game but a good one. Select words to draw and illustrate their meaning. For example, "FIRE" and "SLIME" are drawn to illustrate what these **adjectives** describe. You can illustrate **nouns** too, such as "FISH," and "BOXES" and "CIRCLE." Use colored pencils or markers for the full effect—imagine slime and fire in color!

To get you started, here are some words to illustrate: curly
barbed-wire
irritated
snakes
hairy

Fill this page and another sheet of paper with your own language art!

Graffiti is form of self-expression that can range from names scratched into wet cement to elaborate spray-painted murals. Before it gained acceptance as an art form, graffiti was mainly illegal. Most artists used the walls of buildings, derelict trains, and other public and private spaces as their gallery—without permission.

Sometimes beautiful, sometimes offensive, graffiti often covers ugly urban decay. Its artwork and **tags** (a graffiti artist's name, written in a stylized form) provide viewers with environmental, political and social statements, satire and philosophy. Several graffiti artists became successful gallery artists:

Keith Haring drew chalk pictures on the black paper used to fill empty advertising space in the New York subways.

Jenny Holzer pasted sheets of her **Truisms**—a list of beliefs—on walls and poles in very public places. Her Truisms appeared on the giant Matrix board in Times Square and were engraved into marble benches for a gallery show.

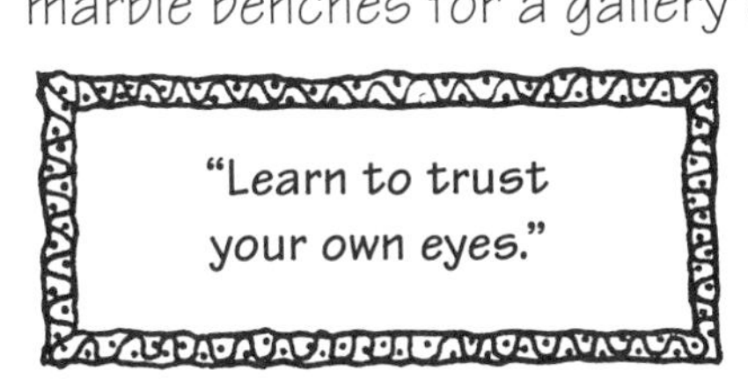

One of Jenny Holzer's Truisms.

Other artists who brought attention to graffiti include Barbara Kruger, Kenny Scharf and Jean-Michel Basquiat.

Graffiti doesn't have to be a crime. Be sure to limit street art to approved sites!

IDEAS

Gorgeous chalk drawings can decorate sidewalks and walls. You could work with lines and flat colors or do blended impressionist scenes. (Remember Mary Poppins?) You can use stencils by dipping a stiff brush into chalk dust and dabbing inside the stencil.

Photocopy drawings, prints, photographs or poetry to paste or tack to approved sites (like community bulletin boards, school halls, boarded-up buildings). Try using neon papers or making multiple copies for greater impact.

For festive street art, try weaving into chain link fencing with brilliant crêpe papers or fabrics. You could paint long sheets of kraft paper, then cut them into 3" strips for weaving. Artist David Finn used plastic bags to shape human figures into chain link. Incorporate a variety of materials into fence weaving—sticks, reeds, balloons, foam—the possibilities are exciting!

Pictography

See if you can write a note with pictures (pitchers).

Write an interesting and descriptive sentence. Now write the sentence using pictures instead of words whenever possible. Think of ways to illustrate the words.

Add letters: b+ = brake or break

Subtract letters: – at = go

Illustrate: hand can fish

Use homonyms: = knows

t + is 2 it!

That's all (awl) there (thair) is to it!

Use a sharp pencil, a good eraser and your language arts skills. Enjoy!

the Dog's Domain

Maps are fun to look at and make. There are road maps, topographic maps, treasure maps, maps of the ocean floors, theme parks, the human body, outer space and many more.

This is a map of a dog's domain. It shows all the details about the yard that are important to her!

Get a sheet of paper and a really sharp pencil, and make a map. Choose something you know well—something you see a lot: your neighborhood, playground, or the route to and from school.

Things to think about:

Include borders, illustrations and a fancy compass—one that reflects the subject of your map. The compass above would work with the dog's domain.

Ink your drawing with waterproof ink. Let dry. Erase pencil lines, then add watercolor.

* For inspiration: look at "National Geographic's" maps. They're the best.

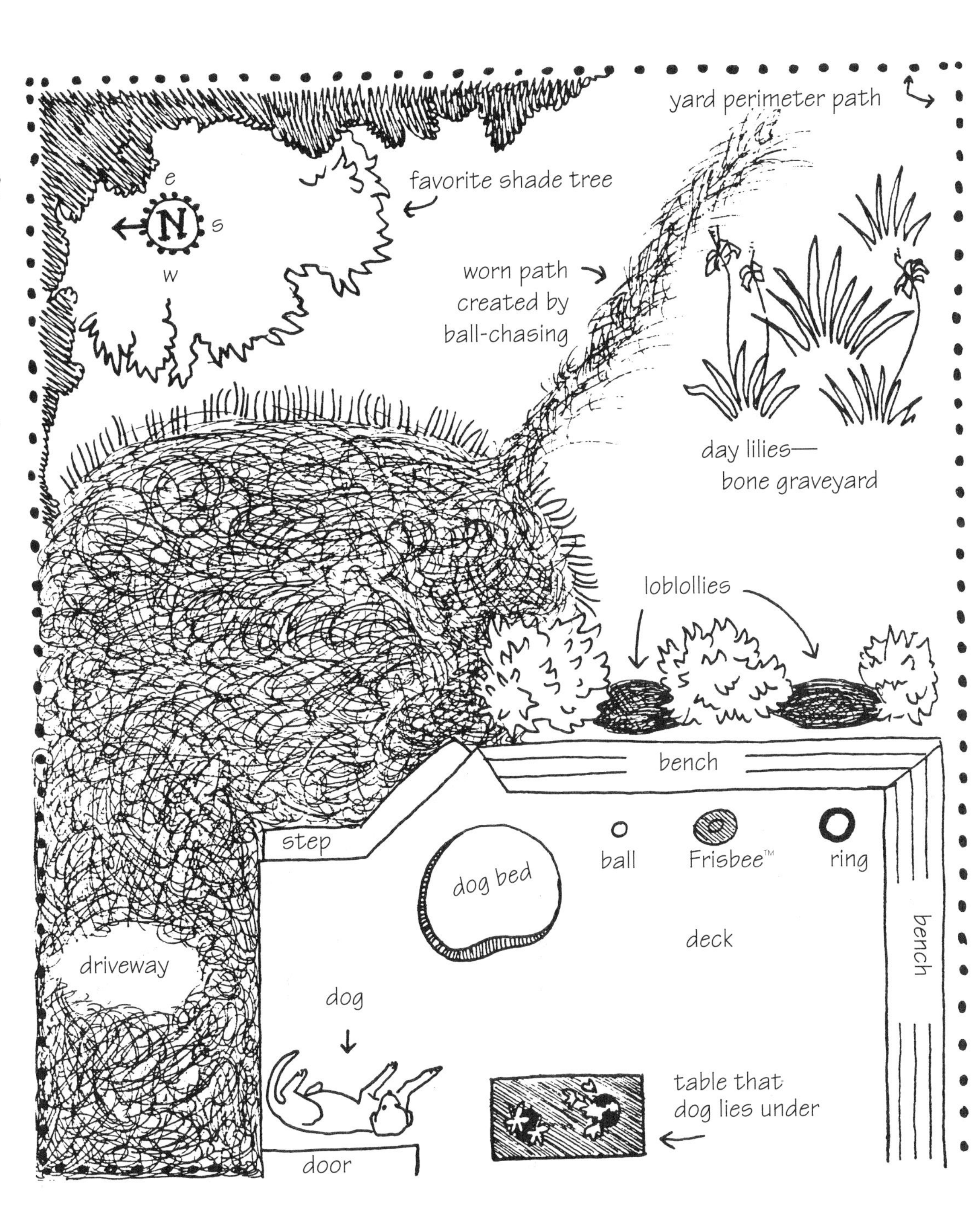

Posters attract attention and provide information in a visually exciting way. Art, travel, celebration, theater, events, advertising, music and the environment are just some of the many subjects of posters. Poster designs usually combine artwork with **typography** (letters). Check out graphic design and illustration annuals at your public library for world-class examples.

Design a poster. Use at least an 18 x 24" sheet of paper. The design must include artwork and three lines of type that vary in size. You can add a border design if you choose. Use any materials you want. Tempera is an excellent choice for poster paint because of its vibrant, flat colors. Tempera mixes and layers well and can easily be combined with other media, like collage, pastels and markers.

Make your artwork fill the space well. Don't make tiny drawings. You want your design to be visible from across a room.

The most important words (the what) are usually larger than the "particulars" (when, where, etc.).

A great way to start a poster design is to mark where the **copy** (written information) will go. Use guidelines to help you draw the letters and words straight. **Guidelines** help lay words out in an arc or shape, too. Draw the words onto the guidelines, and fit your artwork around the words.

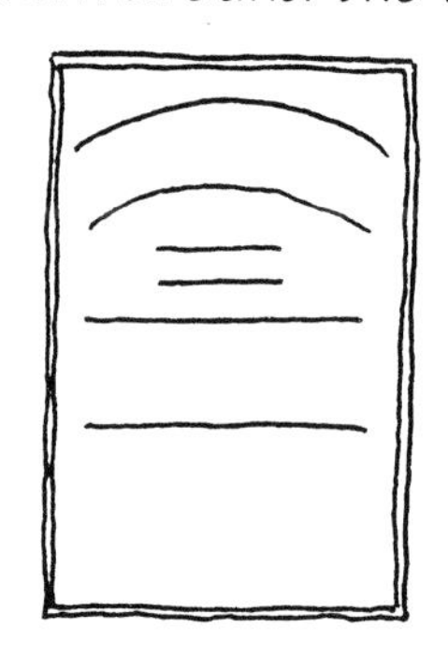

You can also draw the artwork first. Leave room for the copy to be added later, like inside the king's robe.

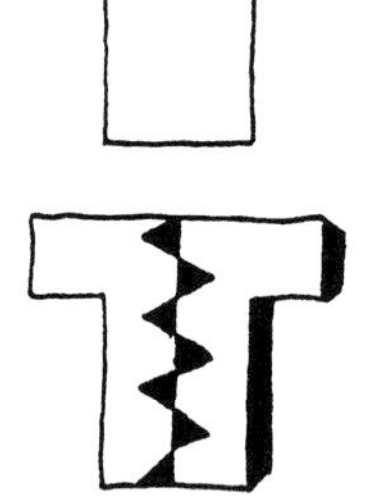

Stencils can be used to lay out letters. You can change plain stencils by decorating the inside of the letter or by changing its shape altogether.

Even if you plan to draw your letters free hand, it's a good idea to use guidelines to keep the height, width and space between letters uniform.

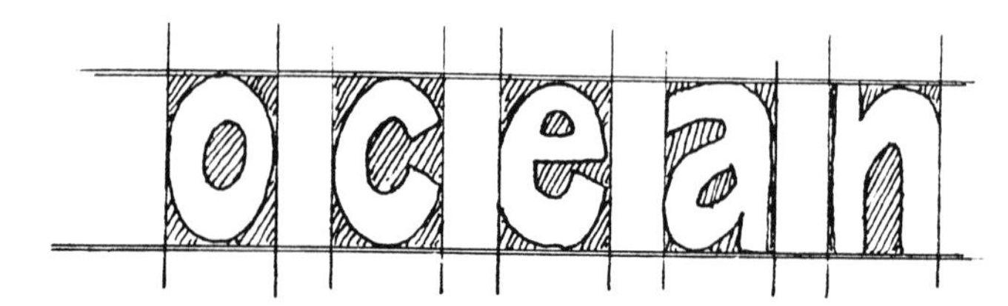

Make sure your typography is appropriate for your artwork and message. For example, you wouldn't use a flowery, fancy script for a rodeo poster. Study typography in books and magazines for ideas and inspiration.

Menu Madness

Everyone loves a menu that's fun to look at. Design a menu for a restaurant. You can incorporate the clip art below or other clip art. Enlarge, shrink, repeat and cut apart clip art for creative use. (For example, you can cut the cookie out of the girl's hand and have her hold something else.) Your menu can be folded or on a single card. You can handletter or use a computer for your type.

For the silly menu to the right, the choice of clip art determined the name of the restaurant and what it serves. If you'd rather draw the whole menu and not use clip art, that's even better. Color the menu, add collage, laminate—try to make it look like a real menu (even if it is a funny one!).

MAKE A BOARD GAME

Board games are played by people of all ages. They can be simple or extremely complex. There is a **theme** to every game. For example, "Monopoly" is about acquiring real estate and earning big money. The board represents a real town and includes fancy neighborhoods, railroads, utilities companies and a jail. "Candy Land" is about racing other players through gumdrops and lollipops to the finish line. It's fun to make up your own board game. The following suggestions will help you get started.

First, design the path that the players will take. If the game is a race from start to finish, you need to draw a beginning and an end, and fill the space in between with neat things to do. If the game objective is to collect money, tokens or cards, the path could be a simple circle or square, or any path that can be repeated.

Create money, tokens or cards for a more complex game. Make sure the designs reflect the game's theme.

Play money should reflect the theme of the game, like this money from the game "Ponds and Lakes."

Make your game fun to play by decorating inside and around the game path to create the atmosphere. In the "Art Museum," players move through sculpture, portraits, landscapes and special exhibits—all aspects of a museum visit. Make your illustrations consistent within your chosen theme. You can write instructions like pick up a card, jump ahead or whatever you want on the game path.

Now decide how your players will advance. You can use dice or a spinner. Make a spinner with posterboard and a paper fastener. Cut a circle out of posterboard and divide it into sections that give movement instructions. Make a posterboard arrow or other pointing shape, and attach it to the center of the circle with the fastener.

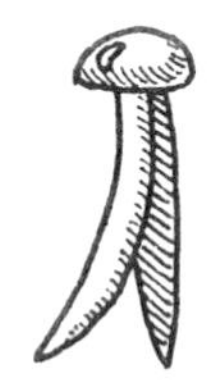

Use a paper fastener to attach the arrow to the posterboard circle. The assembled spinner can then be attached to a posterboard base, if you want.

Look at board games. Study their designs, structure and unique features. Note what makes them interesting. Play your own game, and determine how fun it is. You can always add to your game design if necessary.

Roll the dice to go through the museum's exhibits. Start at the Atrium. Use dimes, peas, beads or other small objects for place markers. The <u>last</u> one to the Gift Shop wins.

Flip Book I

Making a flip book is similar to making an animated film—you combine pages of individual drawings to create the illusion of movement and action. To make a flip book you need: cheap, thin white paper, sharp pencils, erasers and a good, dark fine-point pen. (If you have access to a light table, great!)

For a flip book to work, the paper and the drawings require **registration.** That means all the edges of the paper and the drawings have to line up one on top of the other exactly.

A pad of paper works well because the gummed edge holds the paper in place for registration. (Make sure the paper is thin so you can see through it.)

You can cut sheets of paper to the same size and secure one side with a bear clip. Make sure the edges opposite the clip are even.

How to Do the Animation

Do the first drawing on the bottom page of the flip book. You can draw in pencil first, then trace over the pencil with ink, so you can see the drawing through the next sheet of paper. This is important because each drawing is made from the previous drawing **(a)**. Be sure to draw on the open bottom corner so you can see your animation **(b)**.

Start by trying a simple animation. Make the action happen gradually—this makes the animation flow smoothly and realistically. The "Shade" sequence below illustrates the process: drawing #1 was the bottom drawing, and #7 was the top. After drawing #1, the next sheet of paper covers it, and the shade is drawn a little higher. The window is traced exactly as it is in drawing #1 because it doesn't change. Drawing #3 shows the shade go up a little more. The window is the same, and the man begins to appear. As you draw, flip back and forth to check your action and registration. Follow these steps all the way to the last drawing.

Clear drawings and simple subjects are essential to beginning animation. You can create a "story" line (a plant grows), or you can work with just shapes or lines to practice and build skills.

Helpful Hints

- Mount finished flip books on stiffer paper like 3 x 5" cards. This will make them flip better and last longer.
- Look at cartoons on video frame by frame. This is the best animation teacher possible (especially if you are looking at early Disney or Warner Brothers cartoons).

Flip Book II

After you make a practice flip book, you are ready to do a character animation. Begin by creating a character. Choose a design that is fairly simple. "Kit" (below) is constructed of ovals and "rubber hoses." Hose arms and legs move easier than appendages with bones. The ovals work well because they are almost the same from any angle. If you look at old Disney cartoons (from the 1920s!), you will see this approach.

Draw your character from several angles. Practice facial expressions and situations: pitching a fit, holding something, sound asleep, anything! In short, work with your character so you'll be ready to animate. This preparation work is very important, so don't skimp on practice here!

It takes about twelve pictures to make one second of animation.

Exercise #1: Do a short animation of just your character's face. Gradually, make the face change page by page. If you change him too fast, the movement will not "flow." Any part of the character's face that's not changing must be traced exactly the same as the previous drawing. When "Kit" gets mad, his mouth and eyes change, the top of his head and ears stays the same, and his chin drops to accommodate the big mouth in pictures 4–8. Each picture is drawn from the picture before it. That's why Kit #1 and #13 are not the same. When you've finished a face animation, try the whole body. Make your character do something simple like jumping jacks or bending over to pick up something.

Drawing People

Drawing people has always been a challenge for art students. Like all subjects, the human figure is best drawn from observation, however, there are a few guide lines to help you get started. Remember, <u>creative expression</u> is as important as drawing the figure accurately. Keep a sketchbook of drawings of people—draw everyday and date each drawing. This way, you will see how much you improve.

Gesture drawings are a great way to begin a long study of a figure. You can do the scribble kind of gesture drawing, or you can break down the figure into shapes and forms. You can also construct figures by using circles and ovals. Use your gesture drawings to assist you in drawing a longer study of a pose.

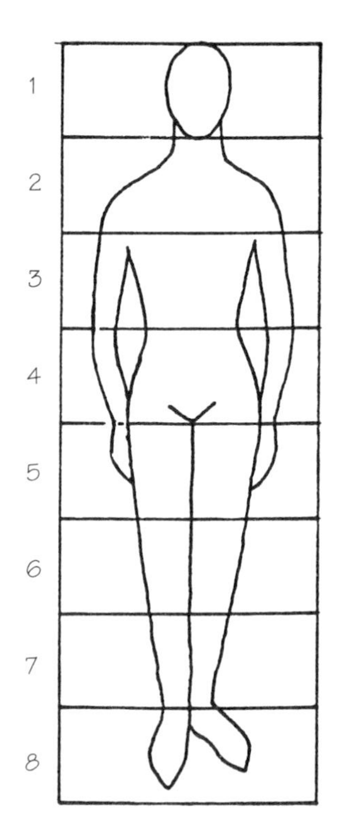

- The human figure is generally 7 1/2 to 8 "heads" long. The hip area is the half-way point. Hands will reach the mid-thigh area.
- Look at yourself in a mirror. See if your body fits the "formula" above. All people are a little different—that's why drawing from life is better than following a formula. The guidelines are just to give you a general idea of the correct proportions.

You can start a drawing by getting the **structural** lines drawn first. These lines can show the angles and curves in the figure's pose and help you fill out the rest of the body.

Helpful Hints

- Don't be too critical of your drawings—just keep drawing!
- When practicing, draw large. Use newsprint and a soft drawing tool, like a 4B pencil or a crayon. Stay loose, and don't erase—just keep making lines on top of one another.
- Block in the entire figure before you work on specific areas.
- Balance figure-drawing practice with quick and longer studies.

GESTURE DRAWING

A gesture drawing describes **action** and **movement.** These drawings are done quickly, which is good because people and animals are constantly moving.

Even when subjects are still, a quick gesture drawing can teach you a lot about figures. Have a classmate, friend or family member pose for you. With sketchy, scribbly lines, quickly build up the figure, and try to finish within a minute. Don't worry about details—just capture the pose.

If you don't have anyone to pose for you, you can do gesture drawings from magazines. Fashion and sports magazines are a good choice.

Do 50 gesture drawings. Fill this page and another sheet of paper.

Drawing Faces

Faces come in four basic shapes: round, heart-shaped, oval and square. Once you have determined the shape, divide it in half vertically and horizontally. These are the axis lines. They help maintain the symmetry and proportion of the drawing.

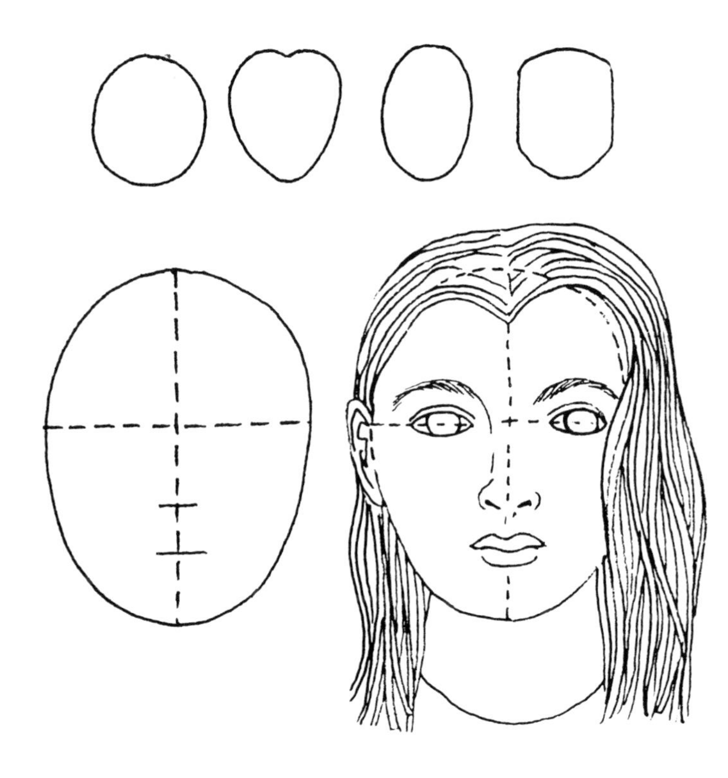

Draw lines that show where the tip of the nose and the mouth will be. Draw ears between the eyebrows and the tip of the nose. Then, add hair along the inside and outside of the original face shape. Draw the eyes on the horizontal axis. Eyes are approximately one eye width apart.

Draw each eye with contour lines—search out the specific shape. Draw the eyebrows in the direction of their growth. Don't draw the eyes too wide open (unless you're drawing a surprised or terrified face). Avoid drawing "spider-leg" eyelashes. White reflection dots in the pupils look good.

It's hard to see true lines that define the nose. The nose is given form by light and shadow. You can still draw the nose with lines, though the effect is not as realistic as a nose defined by value changes. You can draw one or both sides of the bridge of the nose with the end of the nose. You can also draw just the end, which measures approximately one eye width.

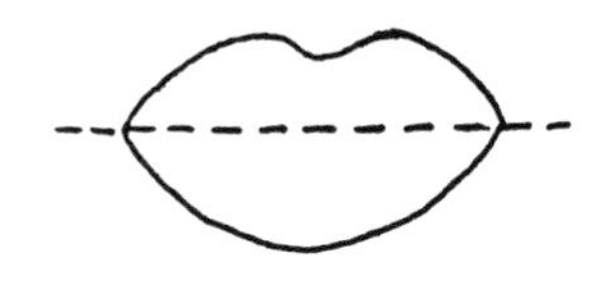

Draw the lips on a straight line. This way they won't be crooked, and you can concentrate on their shapes when drawing.

Avoid drawing "banana lips."

The shape of all lips are determined by five little muscles.

Lips can be drawn with enclosed shapes or open lines.

Try to capture the direction and movement of the hair. It's not necessary to draw every strand of hair, but it shouldn't be a solid "helmet" either. Be sure to draw enough hair so the original shape of the face doesn't look like it has only a few strands hanging from it. Try these suggestions when drawing from your imagination or from observation.

Drawing Masks

Design your own masks. Combine lines and shapes, balance light and dark areas, add details (like hair or headdresses) to change the original mask shape. Repetition is a helpful technique for great-looking designs. Try drawing both human and animal features.

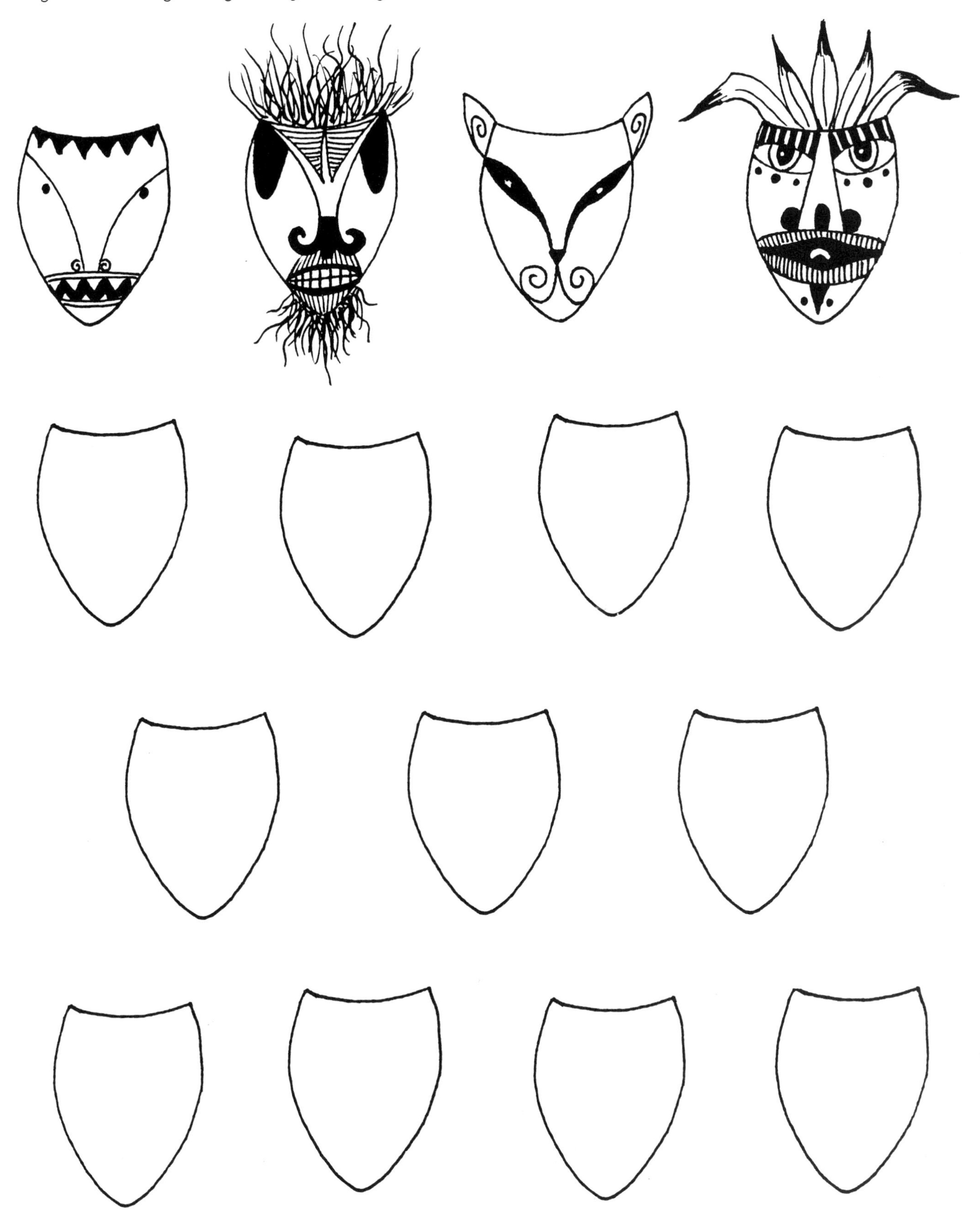

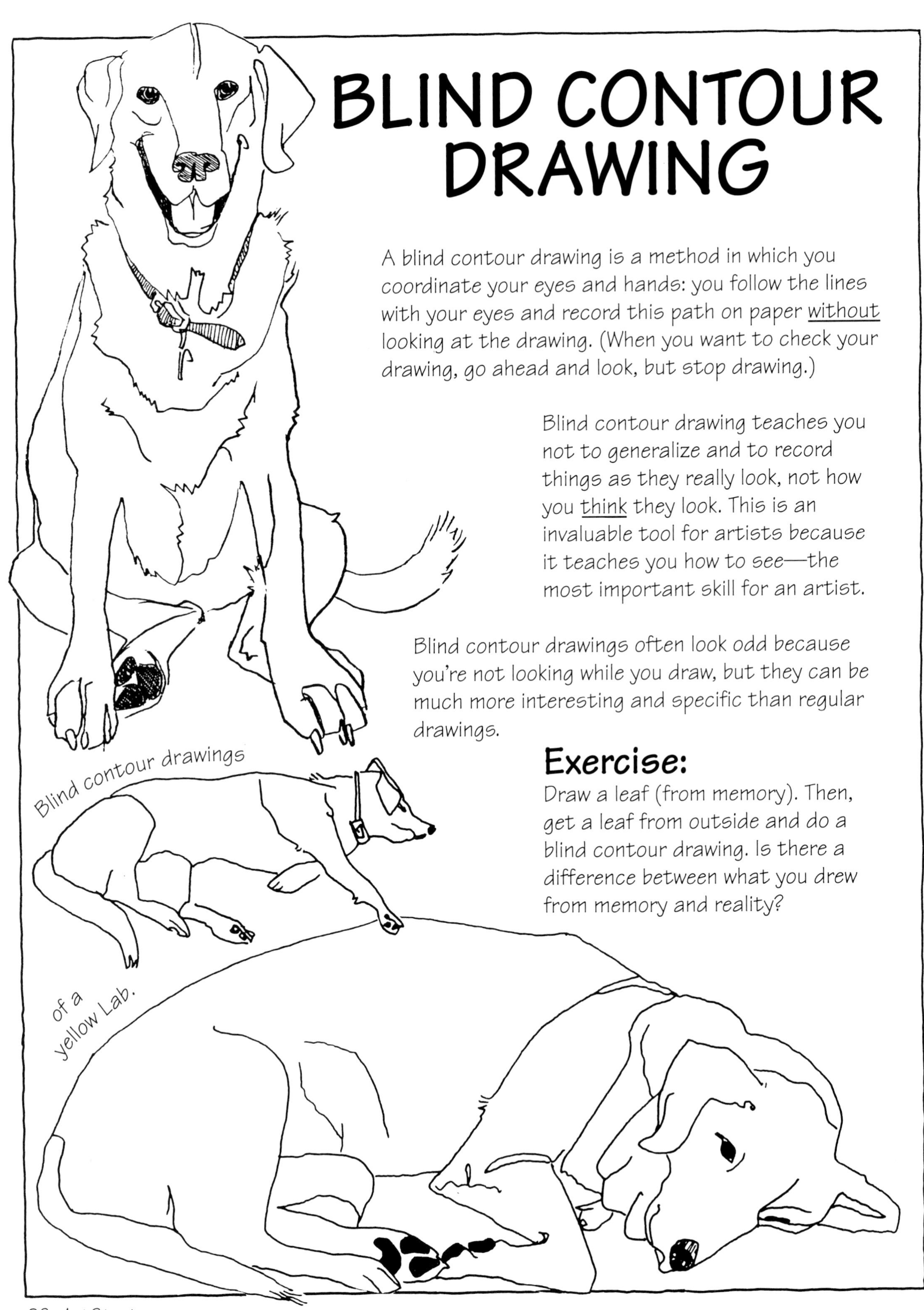

BLIND CONTOUR DRAWING

A blind contour drawing is a method in which you coordinate your eyes and hands: you follow the lines with your eyes and record this path on paper without looking at the drawing. (When you want to check your drawing, go ahead and look, but stop drawing.)

Blind contour drawing teaches you not to generalize and to record things as they really look, not how you think they look. This is an invaluable tool for artists because it teaches you how to see—the most important skill for an artist.

Blind contour drawings often look odd because you're not looking while you draw, but they can be much more interesting and specific than regular drawings.

Exercise:

Draw a leaf (from memory). Then, get a leaf from outside and do a blind contour drawing. Is there a difference between what you drew from memory and reality?

Blind contour drawings of a yellow Lab.

Hi! My name is Hector, and I have an astounding story to tell about the Wind Blend.

One day, there was a sparkling white wind that blew through the area. Nobody knew where it came from. The wind blew over **lakes** and **rivers,** over **seas** and **farms** and peoples' **yards.** It blew through a **zoo** and into the **city.**

As the wind blew over and around animals, it picked up their breath and carried it away. This wind, filled with the breath of many animals, was also inhaled by animals, causing them to transform into blended, **hybrid** animals!

A coyote blended with a rabbit; a dog blended with a turtle and a pig. Some animals blended with up to six other animals. I blended with a chicken.

Fortunately for all of us, the Wind Blend only lasted nineteen seconds before all the animals returned to their original form. No one was able to get a photograph because it happened so fast.

To document this incredible event, we need artists to illustrate blended animals from the **environments** listed above. Make at least ten drawings for an exhibition. The three illustrations below are by eyewitnesses of the actual event.

Chester Woo's drawing of a bear, goose and pony blend seen near his home.

Myrtle Jenkins' drawing of her dog Rocky, who blended with a sea turtle and a pig.

Franklin Washington's drawing based on his experience of blending with a frog.

The Style Game

This is an art history quiz.
You may refer to an art history book.

1 Pick something to draw—a person, animal or object. Draw your subject in the styles of ten different artists. You can choose any ten artists you want. Use any materials you want. If color is an option, your possibilities are greatly increased.

2 See if you can match the illustrations below with the appropriate artists:

__ a. Boccioni	__ f. Miró
__ b. Haring	__ g. Modigliani
__ c. de Kooning	__ h. Picasso
__ d. Dubuffett	__ i. Toulouse-Lautrec
__ e. Moore	__ j. van Gogh

Key: a) 9 b) 3 c) 8 d) 6 e) 5 f) 1 g) 10 h) 4 i) 2 j) 7

Abstract Expressionism

When artist Franz Kline would doodle and warm up for a day's work in the studio, he would make small black-and-white sketches. One day, Kline enlarged one of the sketches with a projector and was astounded by the free abstract images he saw. Kline began to paint large-scale versions of his small sketches in 1949, beginning a series of paintings that would firmly establish him as a leader in the **Abstract Expressionist** movement.

A tracing of Franz Kline's "Mahoning." 1950, 6' 8" x 8' 4".

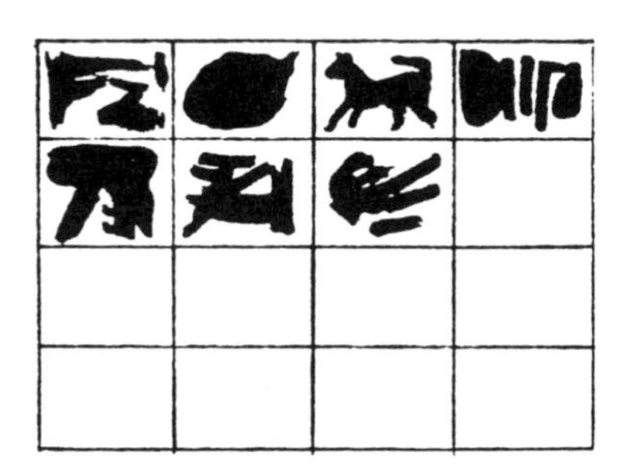

An Exercise

Fold a piece of graph or bond paper to create 16 boxes (fold twice in both directions). With a black marker or a good brush and India ink, fill each box with black-and-white sketches. Consider the white (negative) spaces as important as the black images.

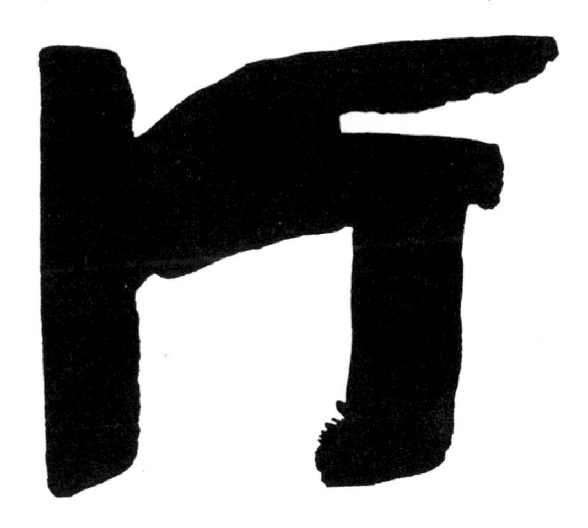

The two illustrations on the left are inspired by Kline's work and the organic shape of a sprouting seed.

Take your inspiration for the sketches from anywhere and everywhere: nature, machines, language, other artist's work, etc. When you have 16 sketches, select one to enarge with a projector.

Project the sketch onto a large sheet of paper (billboard, mat board, many sheets taped together), and trace the image. Paint it in **tempera**. Try combining rough and smooth edges or mixing your own black tempera and painting white areas with white tempera. When you have finished painting, decide: does bigger = better?

a cubist drawing

Try this method for making a **Cubist** drawing—one that shows multiple views of a single object at the same time!

1 Cut three to five sheets of tracing paper to the same size.

2 Choose an object to draw, and draw it from at least three different points of view, but no more than five. The glasses below illustrate three points of view: **(a)** side **(b)** three quarters from top **(c)** slightly below

3 Take the individual drawings and stack them on top of each other. Lay a clean sheet of tracing paper over the stack, and trace all the lines. What you will have is a composition that shows your object from various points of view simultaneously **(d).**

4 Develop this drawing **(e)**, or make a painting or prints. Try incorporating collage elements. Do this exercise with more objects to create a Cubist still life. The possibilities are endless!

LIMITATION

Limitation is the choice to restrict a composition to one design element and is one way to achieve visual organization. An example of limitation in modern art is "Revolution of the Viaduct" (1937) by Paul Klee.

There are many kinds of limitation. For example, Signac limited his brushstrokes to only **dots.** Mondrian did a series of paintings using only **squares.** Many works of art are limited to shades of just one **color.**

An Exercise

This exercise is harder than it looks! It will help you visualize things differently. It will help you generate designs you might not choose when you have more freedom. One result of this exercise is certain: your drawings will be more abstract than usual.

The drawings to the right are composed of only one shape and illustrate a strict form of limitation. Select a shape. It can be geometric, organic or one you make up. Simple shapes work best. See how many pictures you can draw in an hour using just one shape. When you finish, determine if you have any drawings you might want to use or build upon in a future work of art.

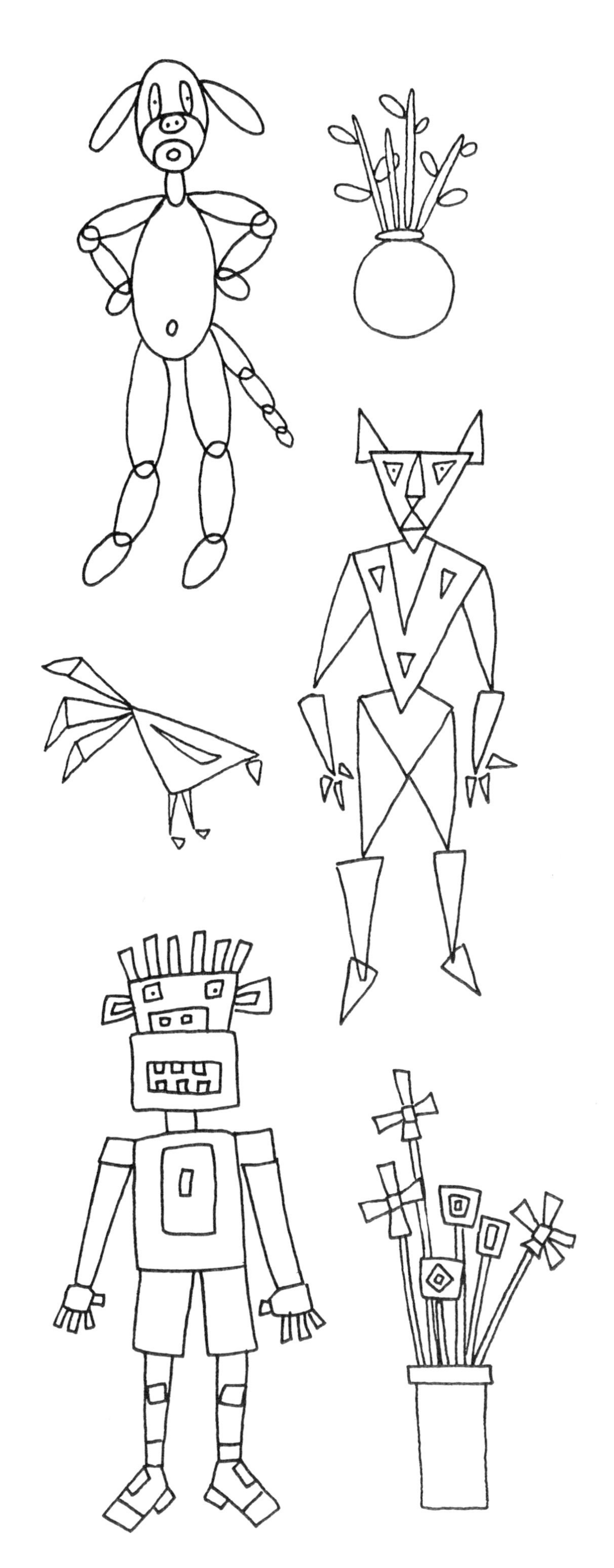

Since the beginning of art, artists of many cultures have abstracted animals. They did not imitate what they observed in nature but presented the animal in a new, stylized way, often reflecting the artist's or culture's aesthetic preferences.

Abstraction allows artists to highlight specific aspects of an animal or to simplify for design purposes. Artists can take what they see and, from there, create something that is familiar, but innovative and unique. Everywhere you look, you will see abstracted animals: video games, product advertising, T-shirts, signs, skateboards, candy, stamps and contemporary artwork.

The next page called **Animal Abstraction II** provides some suggestions for drawing abstract animals.

Frogs
Drinking vessel
West Africa

Bird
Pottery design
Hopi-North American

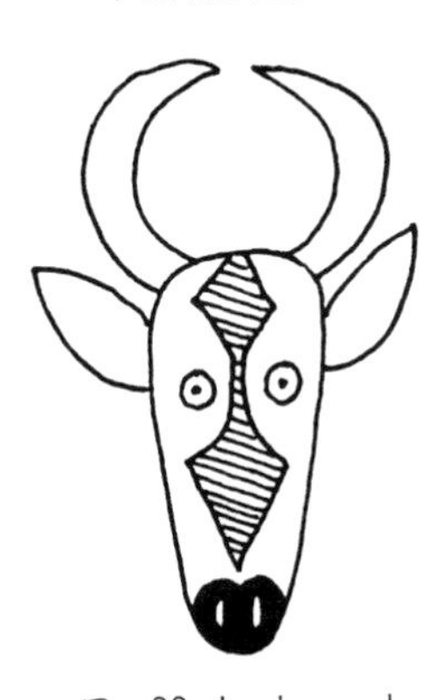

Buffalo head
Mask
Cameroon, Africa

Animal
Textile design
Malaysia

Birds
Pottery design
Pre-Columbian Peru

Beaver head
Mask
Haida-NW America

Bird
Textile design
Siberia

Rainbow serpent
Bark painting
Australia

Dragon
Textile design
China

Draw a page of abstract animals. Abstract subjects can be instantly recognizable or almost **nonobjective** (an artwork with no recognizable subject other than design elements or principles). You can make great-looking finished drawings, paintings, prints and sculptures by practicing abstraction.

Some famous abstract animals in modern art are: "Bird in Space" by Brancusi (1919), "Person Throwing a Stone at a Bird" by Miró (1926), "Bull's Head" by Picasso (1943) and "Cow Triptych" by Lichtenstein (1975). Here are three suggestions to get you started:

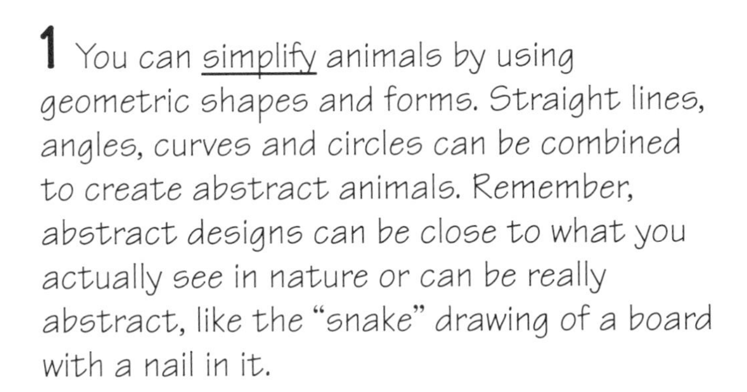

1 You can simplify animals by using geometric shapes and forms. Straight lines, angles, curves and circles can be combined to create abstract animals. Remember, abstract designs can be close to what you actually see in nature or can be really abstract, like the "snake" drawing of a board with a nail in it.

2 Animals can be composed of lines. Pattern, texture and movement can be used to make even realistic drawings abstract. Lines can suggest animal forms very economically (where there is not one line that isn't absolutely necessary).

3 Changing proportions or emphasizing specific aspects of animals can abstract them. You can also eliminate detail or add elements that don't exist in nature.

Aboriginal Design

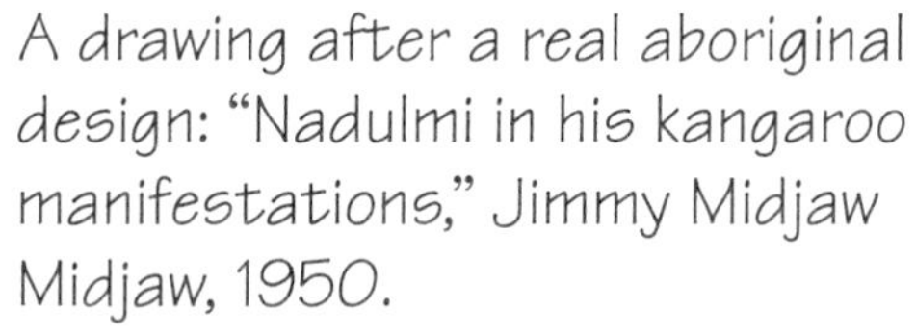

A drawing after a real aboriginal design: "Nadulmi in his kangaroo manifestations," Jimmy Midjaw Midjaw, 1950.

Illustration of a Labrador retriever and bowl of dog food: aboriginal design, North American Suburban imagery.

Aboriginal Australian art comes in the form of rock engravings and paintings, bark and ground paintings, body decoration, and, now, paper and canvas. Most of the work illustrates the relationship between the people and the land, the people and their history, and the epic deeds of creators and supernatural beings. The complex compositions are created by combining shapes and patterns based on a long-established artistic tradition. Certain patterns and designs can only be used by artists from a specified family or geographic area.

To make a drawing or painting based on aboriginal design, follow these three suggestions:

1. Combine shapes to illustrate a scene or event, then fill with patterns.
2. Combine multiple perspectives, e.g., side views, top views, X-ray views.
3. Use earth colors: ochres, reds, dark greens, browns, black and white.

*** Remember:** true art should reflect the world of the maker, so borrow the aboriginal design techniques but not the content.

The Circle Game

Draw as many circular designs as you can in 40 minutes. You can use this page or other paper. Search your visual memory files for every circular image you can! Think of both natural and humanmade designs. Game participants should decide before playing whether designs must strictly adhere to a circle (like the pizza, sand dollar and zinnia) or if you can add to the circle (like the bomb). At the end of 40 minutes, determine:

Who has the most designs?

Who has designs that no one else thought of?

Which designs were the most common?

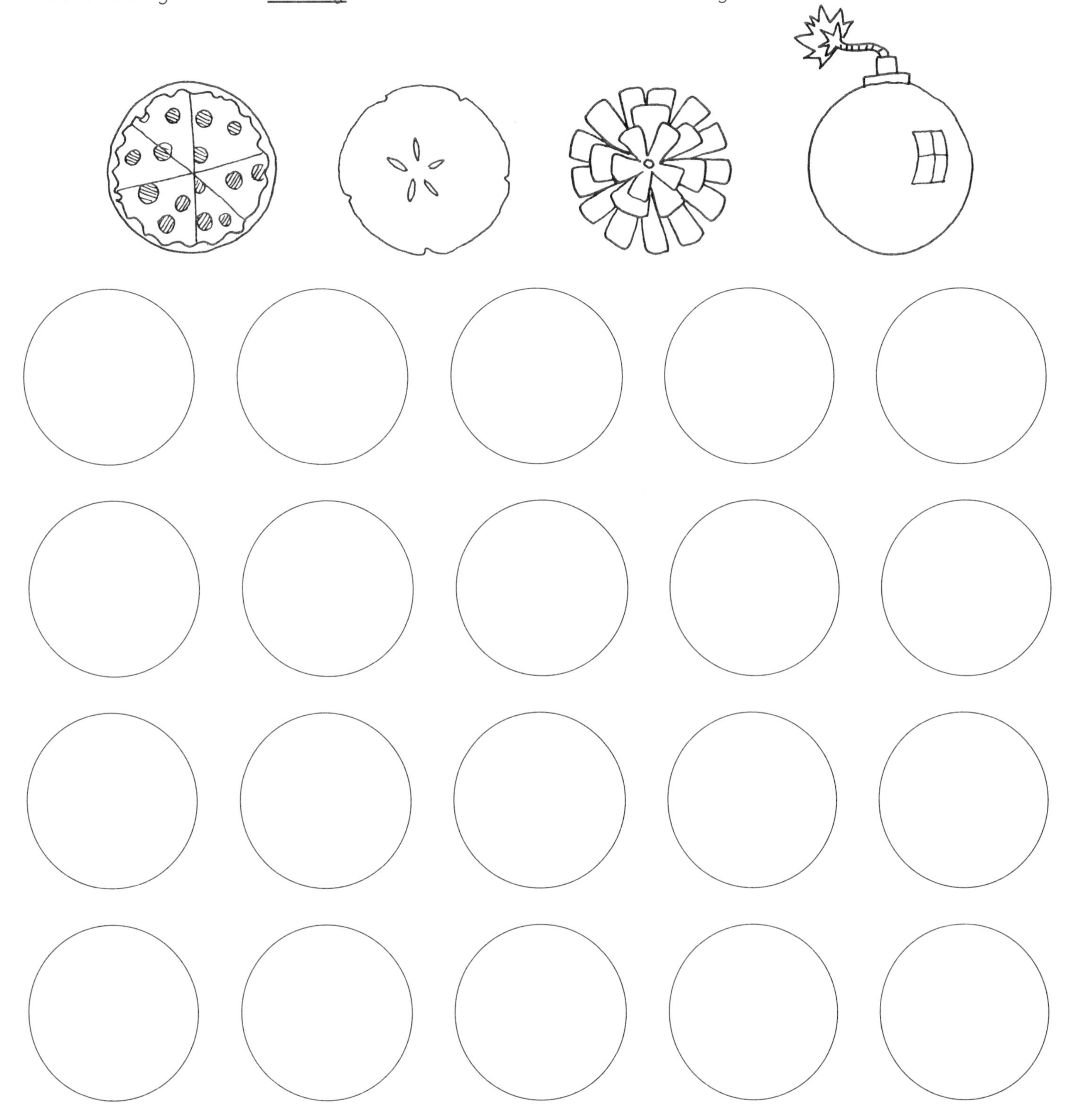

Press On

Have you ever tried printing objects—plants, feathers, fruit, vegetables, fish?

Just about anything with an interesting surface or shape can be used to create beautiful repeat surface designs.

You can also combine prints with drawings and paintings. Feather prints will cover the bird (a), and Dr. Zork's brain is a print of an apple (b). Imagine a drawn or painted tree trunk filled with printed leaves (c).

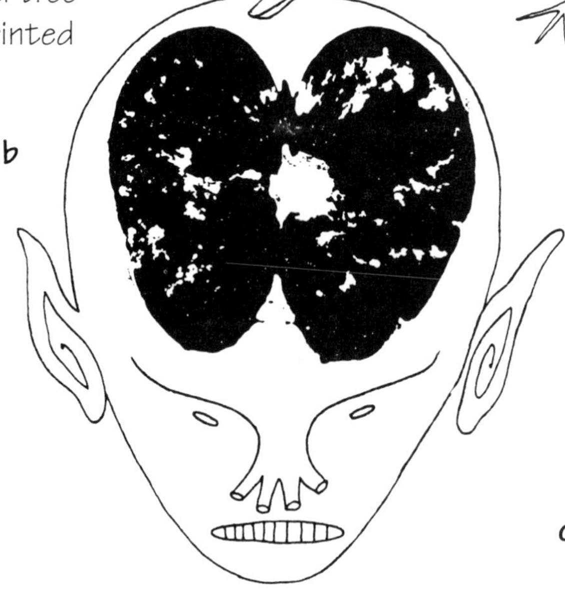

You can print objects by pressing them into rolled ink and stamping. Lay flat objects like feathers and leaves on top of rolled ink, and then, ink the object with a brayer. Lay an inked object down on a piece of drawing paper where desired, and cover it with a sheet of paper. Rub over the object, lift the cover sheet, and carefully lift the object off the paper. The printed image will be left behind with a reverse print on the cover sheet. Save the extra prints for collage or photocopier prints.

(also known as rubbings)

Have you ever laid a piece of paper over a coin and rubbed it with a crayon until you could see the image of the coin on the paper? Well, that's frottage! Frottage looks great because of the **texture** and **high contrast.** Max Ernst was an artist who used frottage alone and with drawing and collage, especially in the series he called "Loplop." Here are some suggestions for making a frottage.

- Get two colors of construction paper: one for the plate, or background, and one for the cut shapes. Create an entire scene. You can glue shapes on top of shapes (like the "House of Loved Pets" below), and you can glue on other textural elements, such as string, leaves or lace. You can also etch into the shapes with a pin for white lines. Then, cover the scene with bond paper, and rub a crayon over the entire design using even pressure.

- Try layering different colors of crayon over one another, or try rubbing with a white crayon on black paper.

- You can cut out designs from finished rubbings to use later in a collage.

Frottage is like printmaking. You get multiples of one image.

House of Loved Pets

SANDED CRAYON DRAWING

People often think of crayons as a young child's art medium. Beautiful crayon drawings have been produced by Picasso, Henry Moore, Miró and Dubuffett. Follow these directions to make a sanded crayon drawing—a technique that will add depth and texture to ordinary crayon drawings. Read this entire page before drawing.

You will need:

- rough, white drawing paper
- crayons
- tempera
- acrylic varnish
- sandpaper
- chalk
- paint brush

1 Make a drawing. It can be a portrait, a still life or landscape. Any subject will work. Draw lightly with pale-colored chalk, or draw very, very lightly with a crayon. Color in the drawing with crayons. Color up to the chalk or crayon lines, but do not color over the lines.

The white lines in this illustration represent the original chalk or crayon line and are the only areas you don't color. In the finished drawing, these lines will be black.

Areas that you want to be white must be colored in with white crayon; areas you want to be black should be colored in with dark blue or violet. Color hard so the surface of the drawing is waxy.

2 Paint black tempera across the entire drawing, and let it dry.

3 Use a piece of sandpaper to scratch the tempera off. Keep using fresh areas of the sandpaper to scratch with; if you don't, the sandpaper will get clogged with wax and paint and will smear your drawing. Scratch lightly in whatever pattern you choose—just enough to lift off the tempera.

You will see your colors shine through the black. Your original drawing lines will stay black because the paint is stuck to the paper and won't scratch off.

4 Wipe off the finished drawing, and brush on acrylic varnish. This will restore the drawing's luster!

Experiment with different color combinations. For example, you could color a landscape in greens and blues and coat the surface with red tempera. The contrast is beautiful.

You could also use scratching tools instead of sandpaper. Paper clips, toothpicks and needles could be used to scratch tempera off crayon drawings. This way, you could scratch in different textures! There are many possibilities with this process.

What About Color?

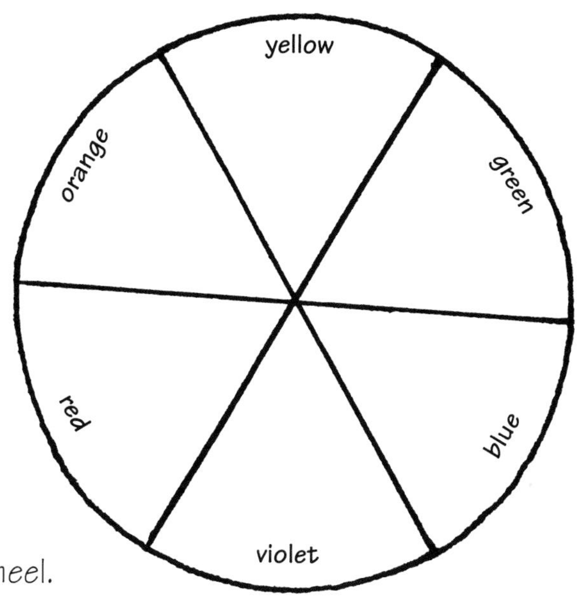

Color is one of the six design elements. It is often the most noticeable element in a work of art. You can complete this activity by coloring in the exercises with colored pencils.

The **primary colors** are red, yellow and blue.
The **secondary colors** are orange, violet and green.

Complementary colors are opposites on the color wheel.
Placing complementary colors next to each other enhances them.

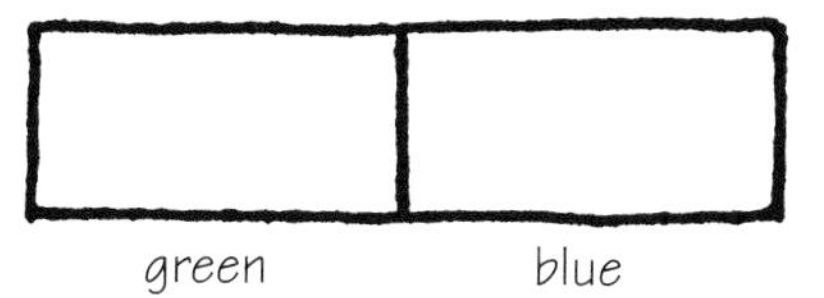

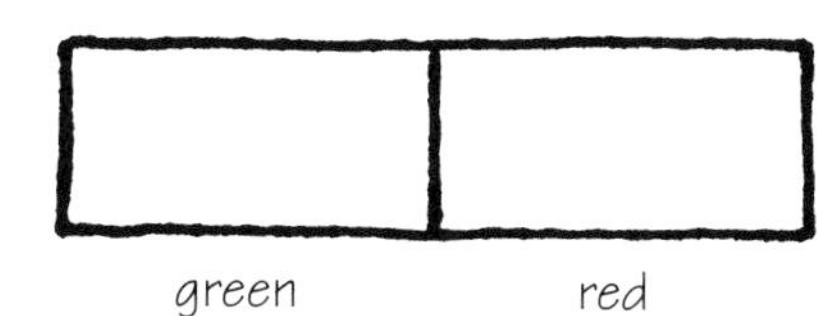

Which green looks brighter?

Intensity refers to the brightness of a color. To lower the intensity of a color, mix it with its complement.

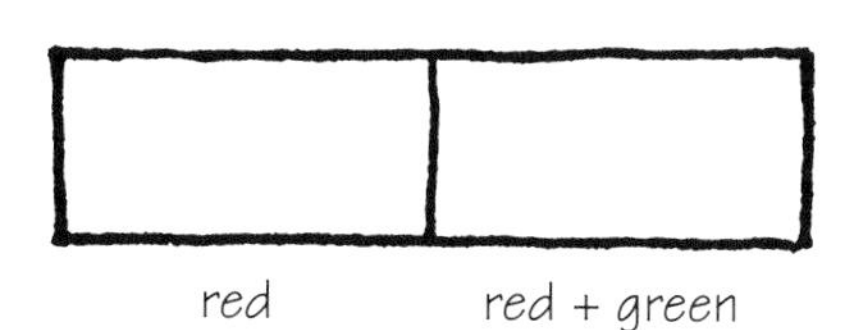

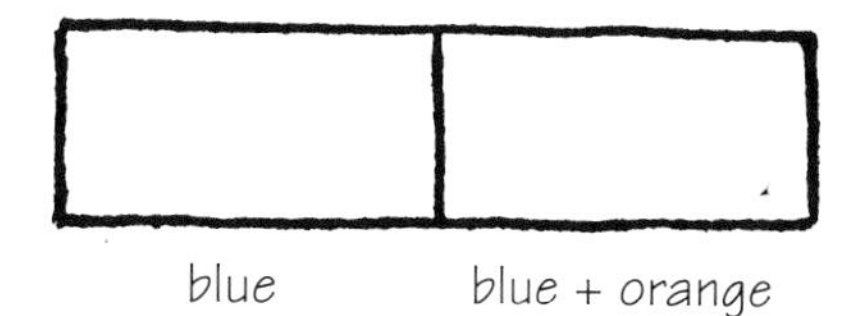

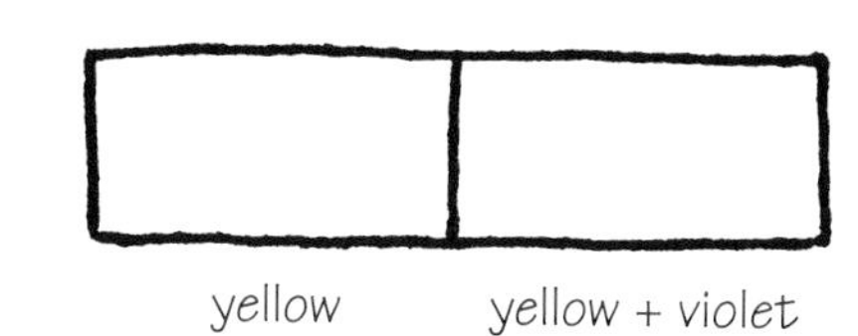

A **tint** is any color plus white.

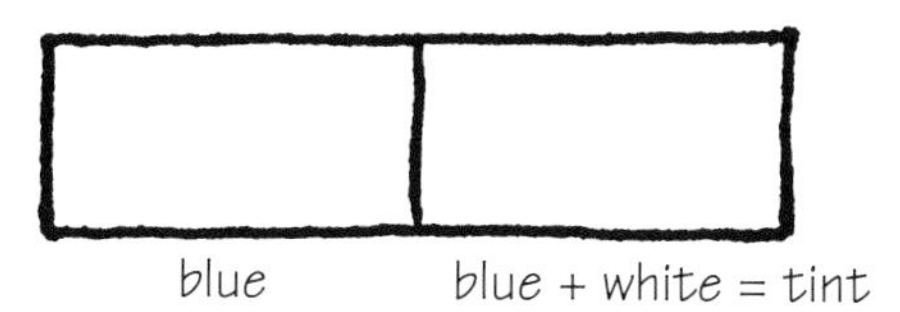

A **shade** is any color plus black.

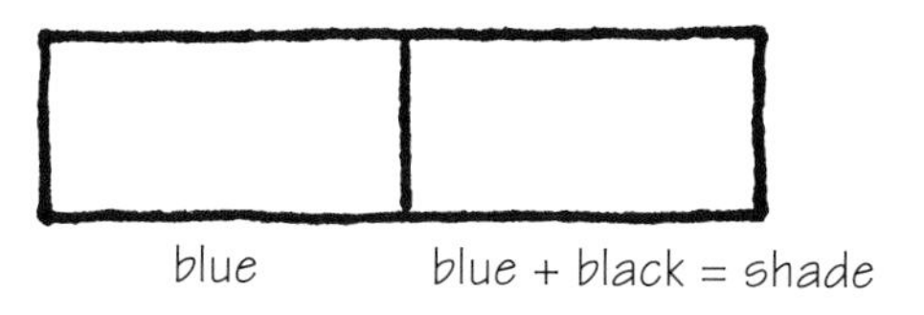

Study **Expressionism, Fauvism** and **Impressionism** for examples of the language and meaning of color.

Warm colors are red, yellow and orange.
Cool colors are blue, green and violet.

Analogous colors are colors that sit side by side on the color wheel and have a common hue. For example, orange, yellow and green are analogous because they all have yellow in common.

Look at color in art by Henri Matisse, Helen Frankenthaler, Mark Rothko, Piet Mondrian, Paul Gauguin and Franz Marc.

COLORED PENCILS

This insect worksheet will make a handy reference guide of colored pencil techniques. Read this entire sheet before beginning. Then, follow the instructions below, and color in the specified areas. (You don't have to use this insect illustration. You can draw your own. Make sure your drawing has at least twelve separate areas to color. Label all techniques and effects.) Apply these lessons to future colored pencil drawings.

The best papers for colored pencils include medium grain (rough) drawing papers in bright white and a variety of colors, bristol, vellum and illustration board. Choose good-quality colored pencils.

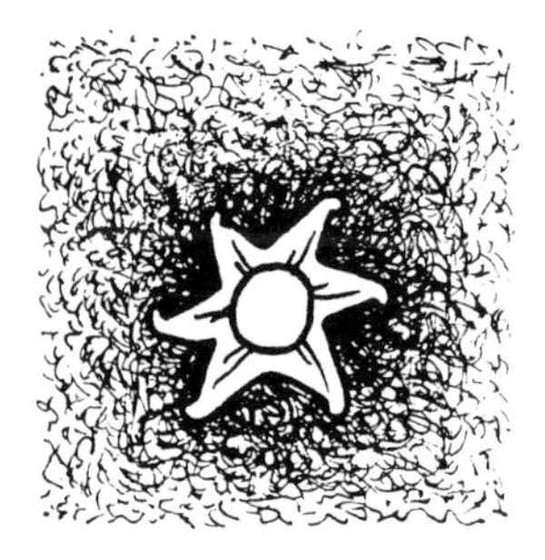

Make the background a value scale. Pick a color and go from light to dark, from top to bottom, bottom to top, side to side, or from the edges to the center like the illustration above. Or, do a **graduation** instead: go from one color to another smoothly.

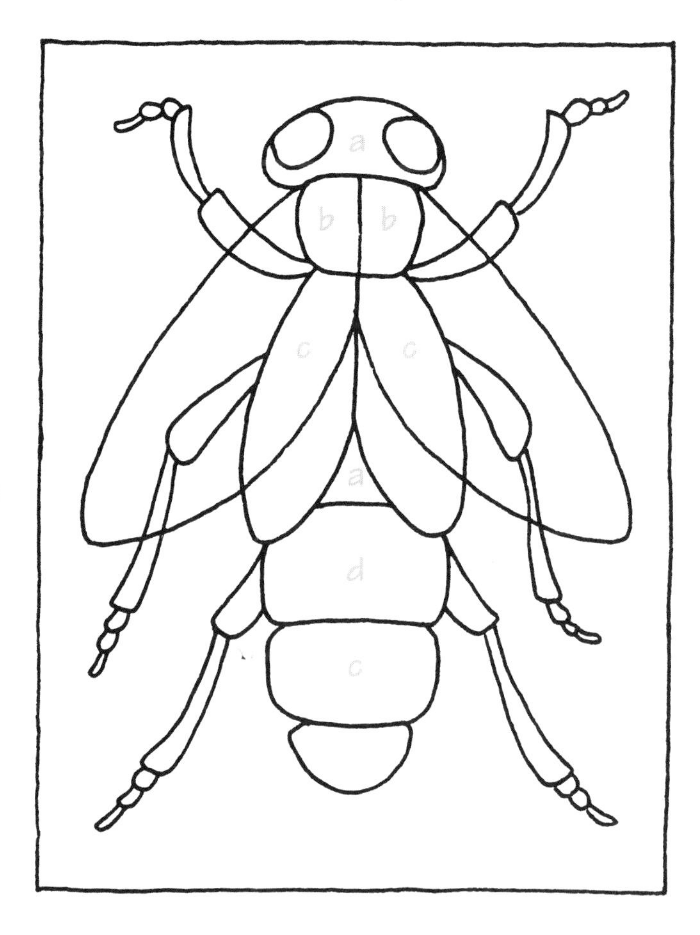

Blend white or another pale color into the wing areas over the background and insect colors. In one area, blend the wing color into the other colors with light pressure. In the other area, use firm pressure and the wing color will **burnish** all the colors together. Which wing looks better? Which wing looks transparent (like you're looking through the wing to the insect?)

Color one of the insect's legs solid black. For each of the other legs, mix black with another color. Which black is the richest?

Contrast is essential for successful colored pencil drawings. Even though there are different colors, don't let your drawings be of one value. Combine rich, dark areas with lighter areas.

Choose a medium-range color and use it to lightly fill the entire insect body. In the marked sections **(a–d)**, blend that medium color with:

a. black
b. the color's **complement** (its opposite on the color wheel)
c. its **near-complement** (like yellow with blue-violet)
d. an **analogous** color (a neighbor on the color wheel)

Leave the tip of the insect body the original medium color so you can compare it with the blends. The best way to blend two or more colors is to layer them one on top of another several times.

THE SEVEN SNAKE QUIZ

Use watercolor or colored pencils to create these snakes:

1. **Value snake**—
   from dark to white <u>gracefully</u>
2. **Warm snake**
3. **Analogous snake**
4. **Cool snake**
5. **Repeat Pattern snake**
6. **(Implied) texture snake**
7. **Complementary snake**

* Decoration and embellishment are encouraged.

Ink Washes

Ink can be diluted and used like watercolor to create **washes.** Washes complement line drawings by adding **contrast, texture** and **depth.** The vase of flowers was painted with an ink wash. Notice how the contrast of light and dark foliage creates depth, making some of the flowers and leaves look like they are behind others. **Spattering** and **dry brush** add texture. The vase looks round because washes were **layered** to darken one side. The light color of the first wash was left on the other side of the vase. Pen-and-ink drawings can be added to washes once they are completely dry.

Painting a wash onto wet paper makes soft, hazy, **impressionistic** images. For sharper edges and clarity, wash onto dry paper. It's a good idea to build up darker values in layers, letting each layer dry in between. <u>You can't lighten a too-dark wash, but you can always darken a too-light wash.</u>

You can use ink washes for **gesture drawing.** It's faster than using a pencil—great for trying to capture poses quickly. You can also begin a drawing with an ink wash to lay out the composition. Then, add detail in pen and ink on top of the dry wash.

Spattering is a special effect that creates texture. Fill a flat paintbrush with ink wash, and drag your finger across the bristles. Spray speckles of wash onto the paper. Try it out on a scratch pad before spattering on a drawing. Spattering looks great in grasses, landscapes, walls, roads, anything with a speckled texture. You can also use **dry brush** to create texture. Dry brush was used to make the ferns in the flower arrangement above. To get a good dry brush stroke, drag wash across scratch paper until the line becomes rough. Textured watercolor paper is the best surface for dry brush, but you can use other papers too.

This is the classic cloud.

Here are six other ways to create believable, lively clouds to brighten landscape skies!

For drawing:

1 Try combining straight lines with rounded lines—clouds often appear sort of flat at the bottom.

2 Make your marks all in one direction to make the clouds look like they are moving.

3 Experiment with pastels:
- Use both the point and sides of the pastels to combine a variety of marks.
- Try smudging some areas while keeping other areas sharp!
- Mix in colors from the landscape below: blues, greens, browns, etc.

For tempera:

4 Paint the sky a solid color. Use a natural sponge or cotton balls to pick up paint and dab clouds on the solid color. Build up value gradually—go for irregular shapes. Mix in grays and blues. Try dabbing clouds on both wet and dry sky backgrounds.

5 Apply cloud color with a dry brush to the dry sky background . This will add a bit of texture and build up cloud color gradually. To soften the edges of the dry brush clouds, reactivate the paint with a clean, wet brush.

6 You can also create clouds by brushing in the sky color horizontally and leaving some areas white.

or

You can create clouds by leaving some of the paper white when you color in the sky.

Look at paintings by the **Impressionists** and John Constable. Great clouds!

Trees—Structure

It's helpful to understand the skeleton when drawing the human figure. Trees are the same way. Careful observation of their structure (trunks and limbs) will help in drawing and painting believable, natural trees.

There's no substitute for drawing from direct observation—so go outside to draw your trees. Winter is the best time to see the limbs. Try lying under a tree to study structure and to observe from an unusual point of view.

What color is tree bark? It's not really brown. When painting tree bark, use a mixture of grays, greens, ochres and blues, or combine browns with colors that gray them down. Trees like aspen and birch are so pale they almost appear white.

Apply paint colors in sheer, overlapping layers to build depth and create a bark-like texture.

Limbs become smaller and thinner as they move upward and outward.

Shading on one side of the trunk and limbs makes the tree look rounder. **(a)**.

Tree limbs don't often come off the trunk opposite each other **(b)**. An irregular form is more likely **(b)**.

Look at trees in art by Georgia O'Keeffe, Ivan Lackovic, Piet Mondrian and Jean Corot.

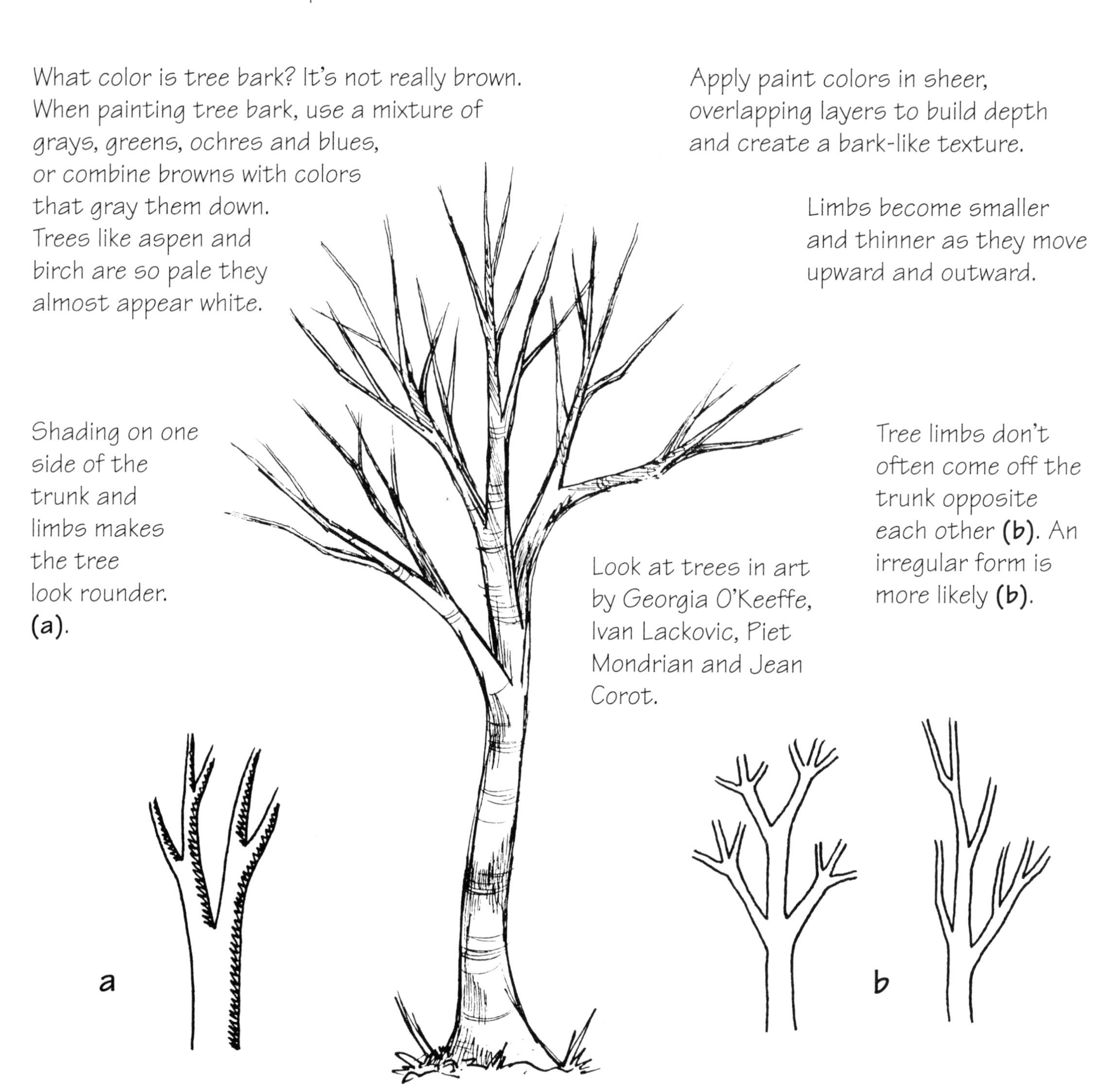

Trees—Foliage

The lush foliage of Earth's trees brings us life and beauty. Trees are astonishingly diverse and individual, making them an ideal subject for artistic inquiry. The seasons are a special treat for painters—from shady summer greens to fiery fall oranges, from stark winter branches to the explosion of new leaves and blossoms in spring.

When painting foliage, see leaves as clusters and groups. Wash in general shapes, and add a suggestion of individual leaves by dabbing on top of the wash. Let the foliage overlap the limbs for depth and realism.

Gray down colors for a natural look—greens used straight from the tube look fake. Mix greens from scratch to produce both warm and cool hues.

Drawing trees in pen and ink offers a variety of approaches. Try mixing pen and ink trunks with ink wash foliage **(a)** or vice versa. You can create many different foliage textures **(b)** by repeating tiny shapes or lines.

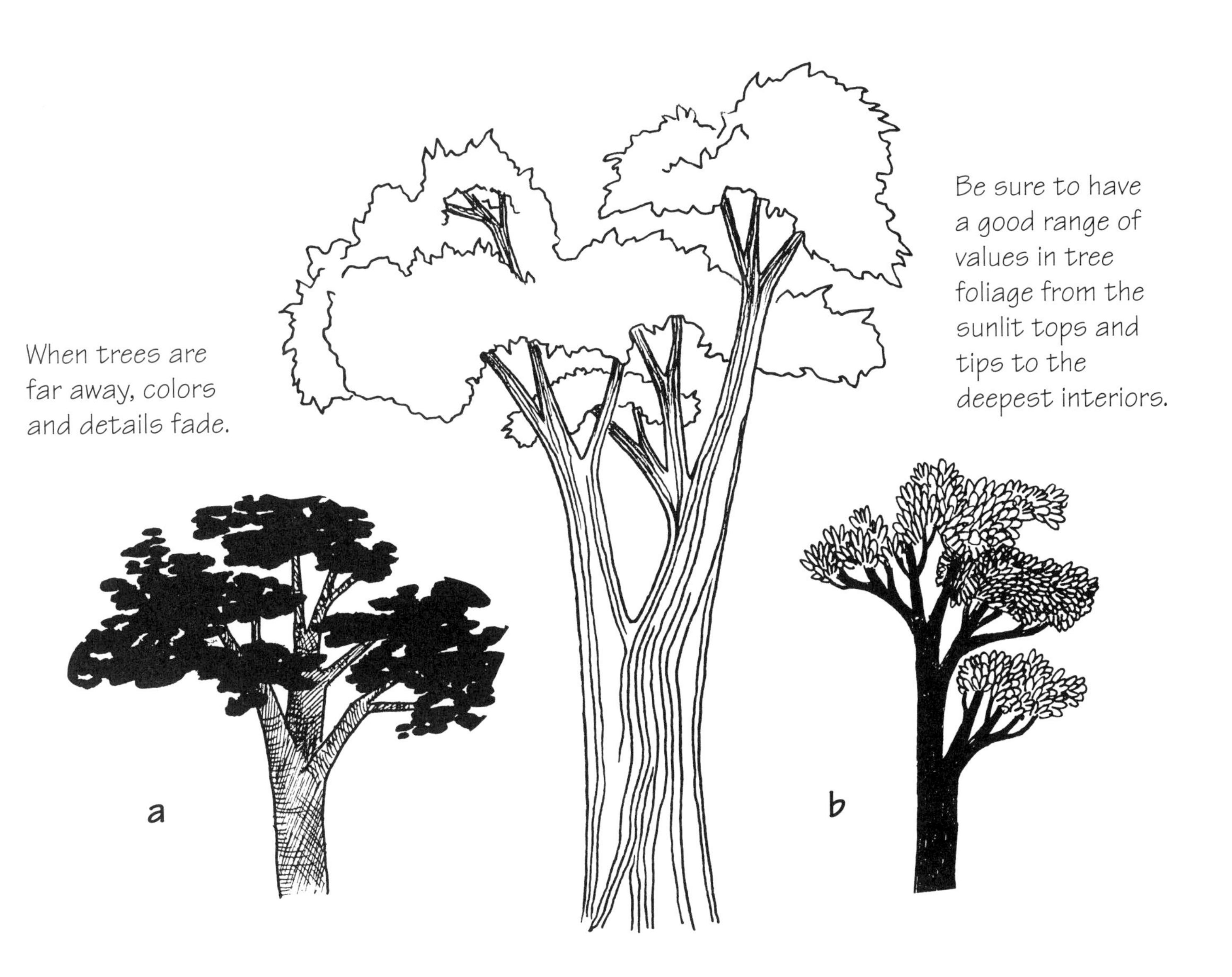

When trees are far away, colors and details fade.

Be sure to have a good range of values in tree foliage from the sunlit tops and tips to the deepest interiors.

HISTORY:

The **Taj Mahal** is an example of Islamic architecture. The style reflects the artistic traditions of Persia, Turkey, Arabia and Mongolia.

In the Middle Ages, Islamic law forbade artists to represent living things on large-scale public art and buildings. That was because only God could really create people and animals and plants, so it was disrespectful to "be like God" and make replicas. This is why Islamic architecture is decorated with elaborate geometric designs.

The Taj was built by **Shah Jahan,** a ruler of India, to memorialize his wife. It took 18 years to build the Taj Mahal—completed in 1648.

It remains today one of the architectural wonders of the world!

YOU CAN DRAW

fabulous Islamic palaces with: squares, rectangles, half-circles and "domes." There are an infinite number of ways to combine these four elements.

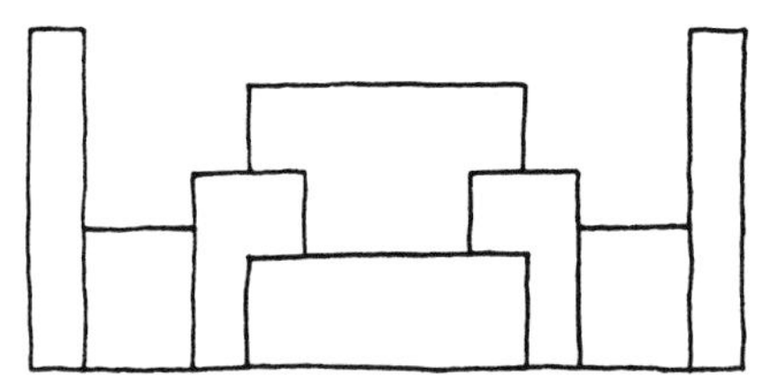

1 Start by building with squares and rectangles. Overlap shapes and vary heights for interest. Don't use a ruler.

2 Add domes and windows and doors.
* If you have graph paper, practice on that. If not, use notebook paper. The lines really help!

3 Add details. If you draw small, keep it simple. If you draw large, you can really create beautiful patterns for the surface decoration.

4 Landscaping and reflecting pools add a nice touch—fit for even the most discerning Sultan! Build whole cities! Have fun!!

Architectural Detail Hunt

See how many of these architectural details you can find in your "built environment." You will have to look in neighborhoods and public spaces. Circle all the examples you find. When you see architectural details that aren't on this page, draw them on a piece of paper and see if you can find out what they are!

Building Plans: Form and Height

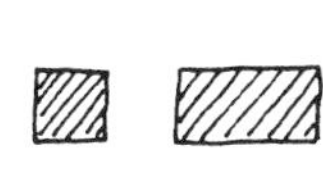

square rectangle

L-shape

irregular

one story

two story

split level

tall building

Types of Roof

gable

gambrel

mansard

pyramidal

asymmetrical

cupola

Foundations and Chimneys

no foundation

low stone

raised

high brick

side

interior

front

Windows

casement

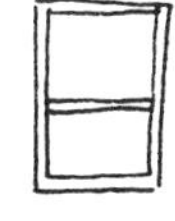

1 x 1

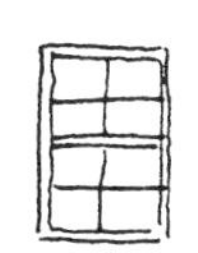

4 x 4

6 x 6

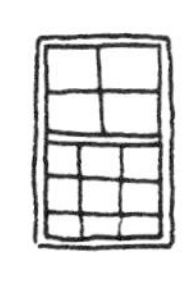

"Mutt and Jeff"

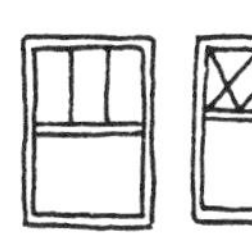

craftsman

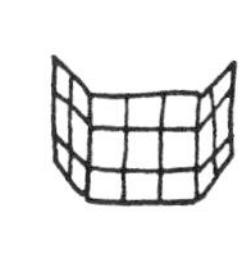

bay

palladian

circular

arch

Gothic arch

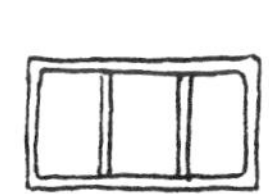

tripart

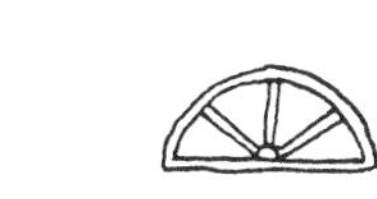

fanlight

Queen Anne

dormer

Columns and Doors

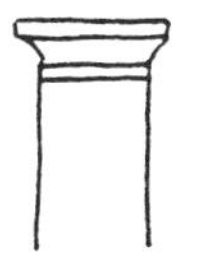

Doric

Ionic

Corinthian

Victorian

plain

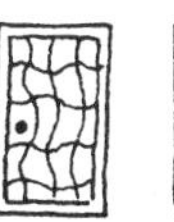

fancy glass

transom and sidelight

decorative

French

fanlight

Building Materials

fieldstone

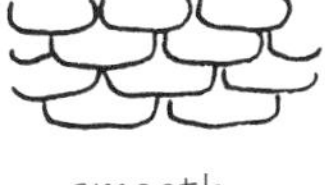

smooth cut stone

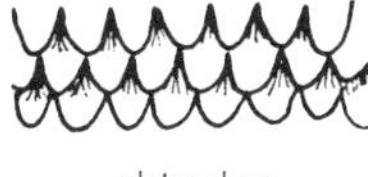

shingles

stucco

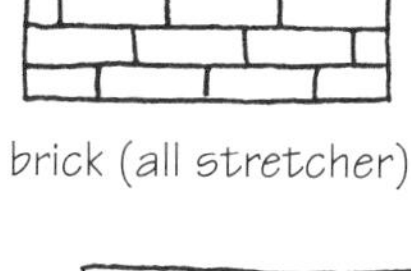

brick (all stretcher)

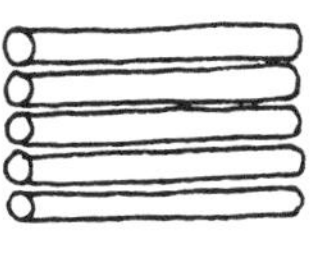

logs

wood or vinyl siding

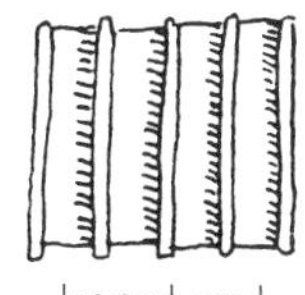

board and batten

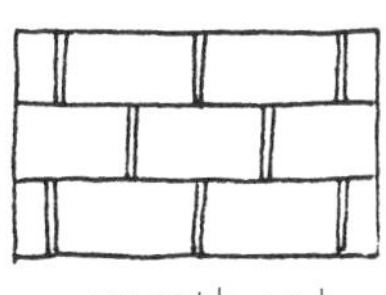

smooth and flush (wood)

fancy brick pattern (Flemish bond)

More ADVENTURES IN LINE • with your host "LINEMAN"

Lines can be combined to make hundreds of different designs and patterns. Using only straight lines, I transformed four identical rectangles into four buildings with character. Try it yourself. Use graph paper (if you have it) and a sharp pencil. Draw some squares or rectangles, and use lines to create a variety of windows, doors, roofs, columns, balconies and other architectural details. You can construct whole cities along streets by using straight lines or by overlapping rectangles like the city below. Line details are enhanced by a good range of values.

Curved and leaning rectangles are the foundation of this lively city.

Accordion books are great because you can flip through them page by page, or you can display one whole side at once by standing it up like the illustration above. To make an accordion book, you need:

- twelve 4 x 6" sheets of mat board
- twelve 5 x 7" sheets of drawing paper
- glue
- scissors
- one 3/4" to 2" wide ribbon

Draw, paint, print, collage or write on each of the 12 sheets of paper. Draw all the artwork vertically. If you want a unified book, choose a theme so all the pictures are related.

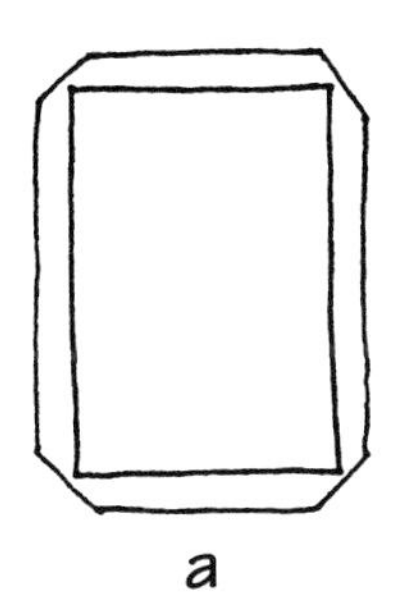
a

Glue the finished sheets to the mat boards so 1/2" of the paper hangs over on all sides. Wrap the extra paper around the edge of the mat board. Make a **miter joint** out of the corners so the folds aren't bulky **(illustration a)**. A miter joint is a joint formed by fitting together two pieces beveled, or angled, to form a corner.

When you have wrapped all 12 boards (panels), you are ready to construct the book. Decide which six panels will face front and which six will face back. Fit them together, back to back, so the front panel's artwork faces you and the back panel's artwork faces your worktable. Decide the order of the panels (for both sides) and lay them out in pairs, back to back. Now, cut two pieces of ribbon 34" each.

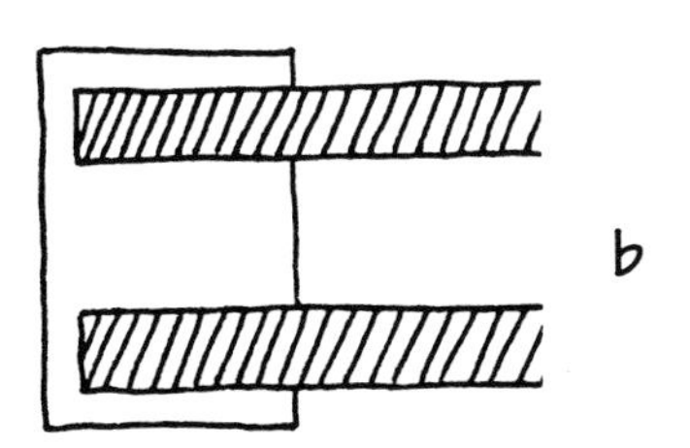
b

Glue the backs of the first pair of panels. Place the back panel face down, and lay the ribbon on it **(illustration b)**. Don't let the end of the ribbon hang over the edge. Now place the front panel on top of the back panel and ribbon, and line up the edges. When you are sure they are straight, put a couple of heavy books on top of them to press them together. Wait 15 to 20 minutes.

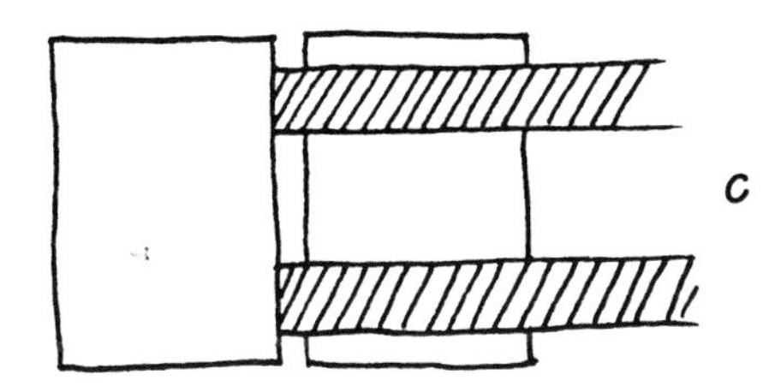
c

Glue the backs of the second pair of panels, and lay out the ribbon **(illustration c)**. Fit the top panel over the ribbon, and make the edges even. Carefully fold the second pair of panels so they are lined up on top of the first pair **(illustration d)**. Gently pull the ribbon tight so it isn't "slack" between the two panels. Press the panels in the folded position using the heavy books. Follow this procedure with all of the panels, letting each pair dry thoroughly. Make sure the ribbon is cut to fit inside the last pair of panels. Now you have an accordion book which is also an artist's book!

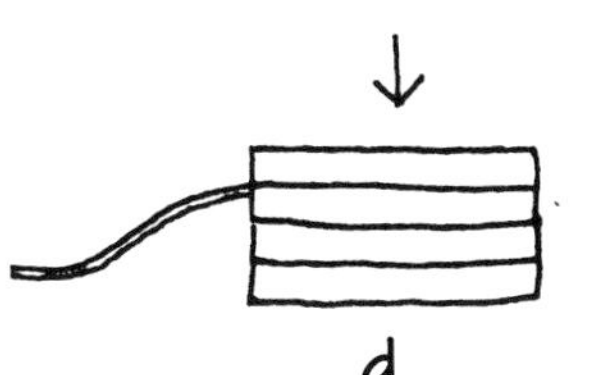
d

To create a gorgeous mask, you need:

- stiff paper or posterboard
- a pencil
- tempera
- masking tape
- a hole punch
- raffia

  and two hours.

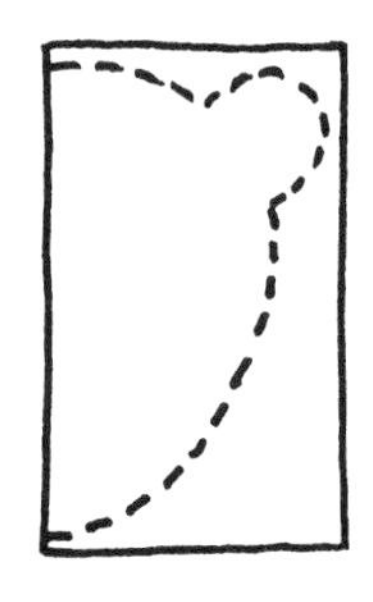

Fold the paper or posterboard in half and crease it hard. Draw half of the head shape on the fold. Cut out and unfold the shape.

Now draw the facial features and keep the design simple. Avoid little teeny details. You don't want to worry about painting around them later.

Select one color of paint to mix with black and white. Choose an earth color like dark blue or green, brown or red, or just use black and white for a gray mask. Paint areas that come forward, like the nose, forehead and cheekbones, with a lighter tint of your color (mix it with white). Paint the eyes, below the cheeks, along the nose and any other area that **recedes** a darker shade (mix your color with black). Limiting the mask to values of a **single hue** will make the mask look carved and **three-dimensional.**

When the paint is dry, add details like whiskers or decorations—or leave it plain like the mask to the left. Use the hole punch to make holes along the edge of the mask. String raffia, yarn or other materials through the holes. You can use food coloring or ink to dye natural raffia a color that matches your mask.

To make a hanger for the back of your mask, loop a piece of raffia or yarn. Tape it on the back of the mask, near the top and on the crease. That's it!

how to make a GREAT STUFFED FISH

* Read this entire sheet before beginning.

Draw a simple fish shape that goes to the edges of a 12 x 18" sheet of white or construction paper. Make the mouth of the fish on the edge of the paper and about five inches long **(a)**.

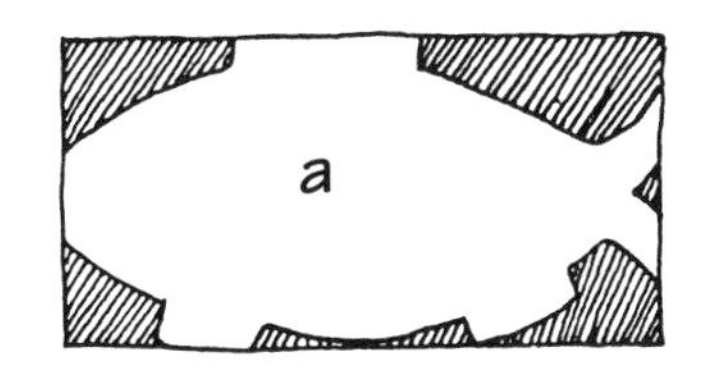

When both shapes are finished and are completely dry, you can begin stapling them together starting at the tail. Follow the main body of the fish—don't staple around the fins and tail **(b)**.

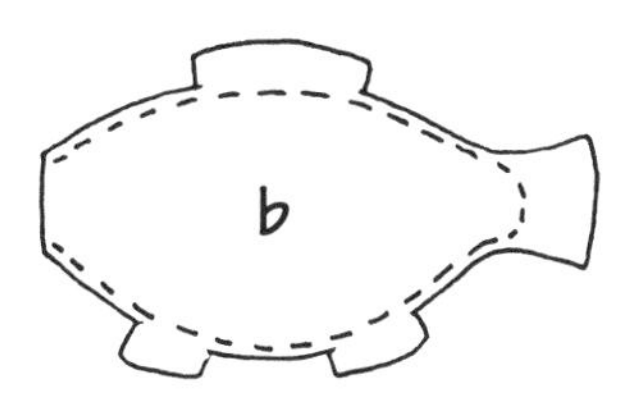

Cut out the fish shape, and use it to trace another one, so you have two shapes that are exactly the same. Fit the two shapes together, then put an "x" on the inside of both shapes. This way, you'll be sure to draw or paint on the sides of the fish that are going to show.

Draw or paint the fish shapes. You can look up the actual designs of real fish to copy, or create your own designs. You could make each side different, but Great Stuffed Fish look best if both sides have the same design.

You can add fins to the side. Cut out shapes, and paint them, let the shapes dry and then glue them to the fish body. You can also add glitter to your designs for a "fishy shimmer". Glitter looks good when it works with your design, so use it sparingly and with purpose!

Staple about one third of the fish, and stuff it with wads of newspaper. Don't try to stuff huge pieces of paper in the fish—lots of smaller wads work better. Be careful not to stuff so hard that you rip the staples apart.

When the tail section is fat and full, staple up a little farther and stuff. Fill the entire fish, but don't staple up the mouth. Pick a color of tissue paper that looks good with your design, and stuff that into the mouth of the fish to hide the newspaper.

Now, hold the fish by the top fin in different places until the fish is level. That's where you punch a hole. Now, thread a string through the hole, and hang up your Great Stuffed Fish!

El Día de los Muertos is the annual Mexican observance of All Saints and All Souls Days. They are days of prayer with many rituals that will entertain visiting family spirits! Family members clean and decorate graves, build altars of food, candy and flowers, and sit by candlelight in the graveyards—singing, praying and visiting with friends. There are special toys created for the days of the dead, like this happy **calavera** (skeleton or skull). Here's how to make one:

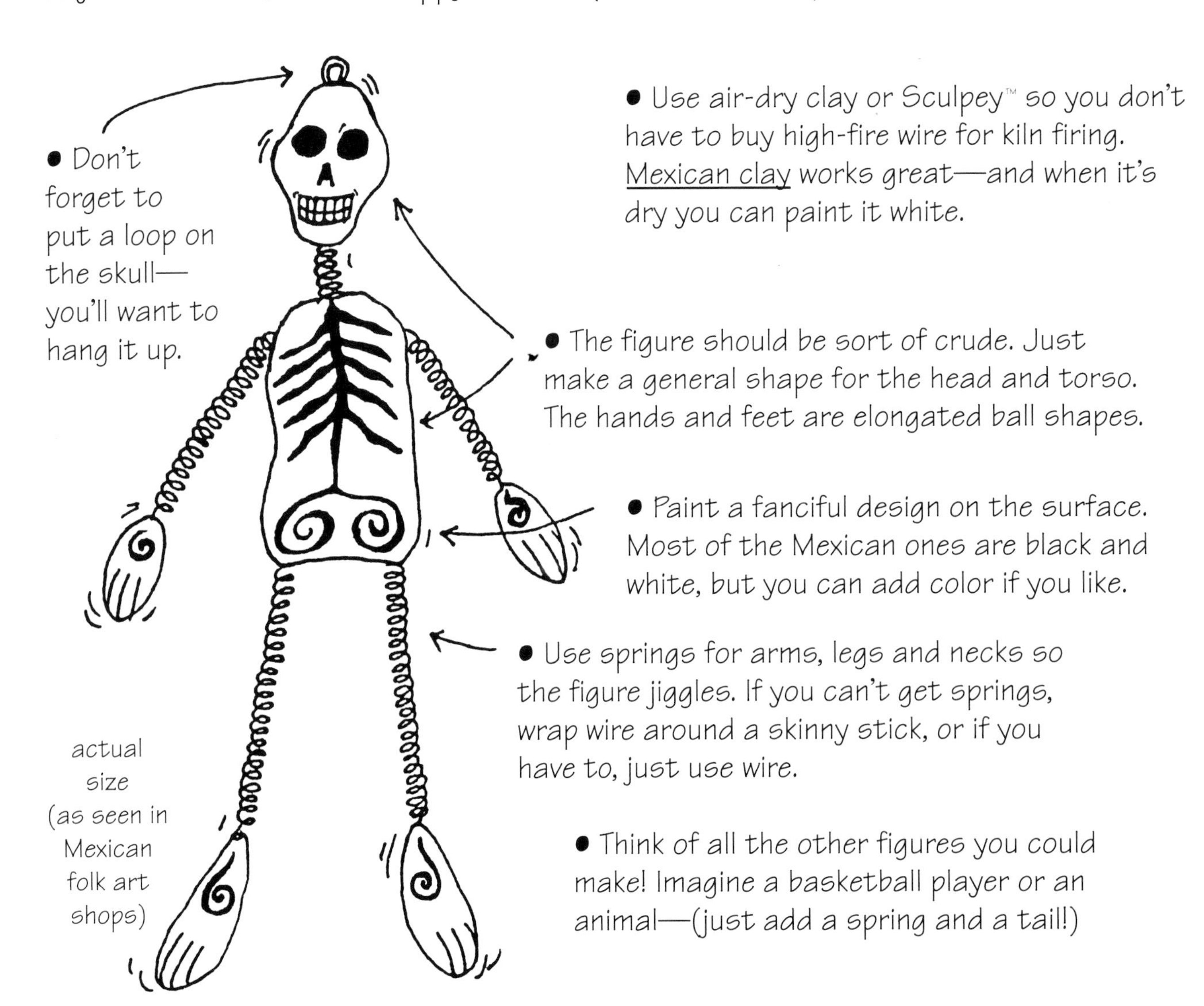

During festivals in Mexico, homes and **zocolos** (town squares) are decorated with fantastic paper banners of cut tissue paper. A banner of **papel picado** (perforated paper) holds twelve or more individual tissues that are glued to a string. Traditionally, the banners were handcut; now, the intricate designs are created with stamping tools. To make a papel picado banner, you will need: tissue paper, glue, string, pencils, ruler and an X-acto knife with a #11 blade.

Cut a variety of colors of tissue paper to 9 x 12". Fold the tissue so it measures 9 x 6". Draw a 1" border on the top and a 1/2" border on the side and bottom. Don't draw a border on the folded edge.

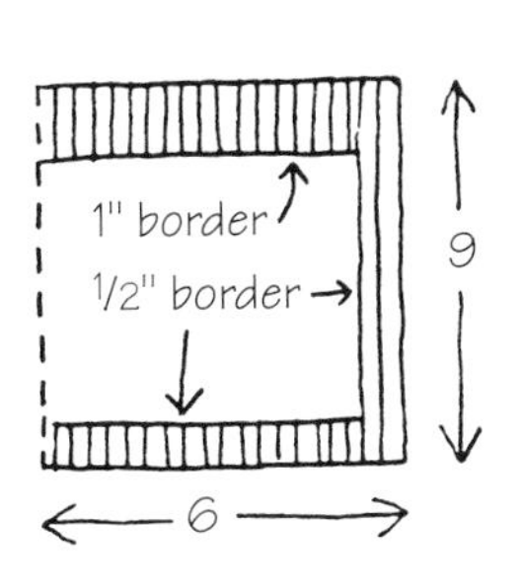

Draw a design within the borders. For papel picado to work, you must attach your designs to the borders or else when you start cutting, the designs will just fall out. The bird design is anchored to the borders by its beak, feathers, feet and tail. The black areas are the areas that will be cut away with the X-acto knife. When the tissue is unfolded, the design will show two birds.

To make a single design, you have to cut only half of the image into the folded tissue.

1 Note how the bird's feet anchor the wing and tail to support the inside areas.

2 Intricate designs can be cut into the solid areas.

3 If you leave a wide bottom border, you can cut a design into that.

4 Any subject can work with papel picado. This cityscape design is strongly anchored on the borders and the fold, and is supported in the interior by the walkways.

To make a banner of papel picado, fold the top border of each tissue in half. Cut enough string to hang all the tissues with 2–3 inches between each with enough string left on both ends to hang up the banner. Dot glue along the fold of the first tissue, and put the string into the fold. Glue the rest of the tissues to the string the same way.

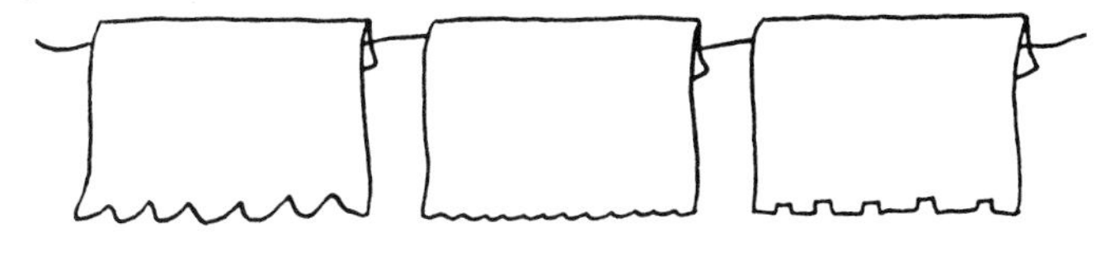

Remember: Form follows function. That means the designs are determined by the need to anchor the image to the borders.

JAPANESE DRY GARDEN

A dry garden usually consists of rocks or stones and gravel or sand. The **placement** of the stones and the lines drawn in the sand create a composition that provokes **meditation.**

The composition of a dry garden should reflect:

simplicity
purity
balance
harmony

and can represent anything.

* Finding many levels of meaning in the composition is desirable!

A dry garden can represent anything from an entire universe to the island of Japan and the sea. "Ryoan-Ji" in Kyoto has been interpreted as a lioness and her cubs swimming across the water.

Zen-Buddhists practice meditation by raking perfect lines in dry gardens. Total concentration on this task will bring insight and enlightenment!

This garden is a shoe-box lid with sand and stones from a river. The rake was constructed of toothpicks.

When making your own dry garden, remember these **Zen** things:

- Select stones carefully—search out the best you can find. Have some that are predominantly horizontal and some that are vertical. In one Japanese garden, this was the tortoise, and this was the crane. They will work together.
- Rake lines into the sand—use them to complement the stones. In most dry gardens, the sand represents water. Can you make waves? Rapids? Concentric rings? A geometric pattern? (Do it as perfectly as you can.)

! Every part of constructing and composing your dry garden should be approached with your full attention. Do everything, even the simple things, to the best of your ability!